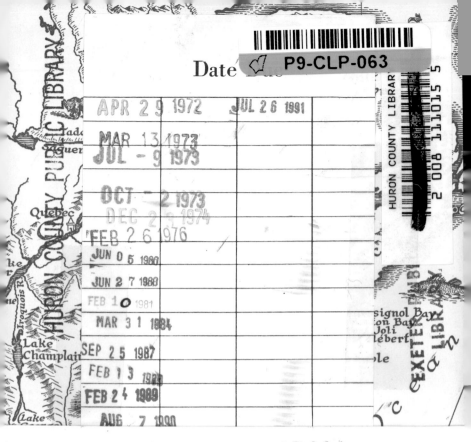

j910
.0924
Champ

Tharp, Louise (Hall) 1898–
    Champlain, Northwest voyager. With illus.
by Charles B. Wilson. Boston, Little,
Brown, 1944.
    250 p. illus.

CHAMPLAIN:
NORTHWEST VOYAGER

CHAMPLAIN
NORTHWEST VOYAGER

BY

LOUISE HALL THARP

WITH ILLUSTRATIONS BY
CHARLES B. WILSON

LITTLE, BROWN AND COMPANY · BOSTON

Fourteenth Printing

TO CAREY
skipper of the *Piper*
and
TO MARSHALL
valiant first mate

CONTENTS

CHAMPLAIN:
NORTHWEST VOYAGER

1 · STORM

THE SKY was still dark, with only a faint trace of color in the east, but already the "salt farmers" of Brouage were gathering on the wharf. They laughed and joked with one another and their wooden shoes made a cheerful clatter. Queer pushers, like solid rakes without teeth, were tossed into boats along with bags for salt. The men turned as hurried footsteps echoed down the cobble-stoned street behind them. "Why, good morning to you, Captain," said one. "Don't tell me you're off measuring and sounding again!"

"Good morning, Nicholas," a boy's voice answered. "Yes — another day's work will finish my chart." The newcomer carried a long roll of parchment and a wooden box which he handled with great care.

"Captain! Who's this you people call 'Captain'?" A ragged blue-eyed boy who had been lounging against the wall of the salt warehouse stepped forward in surprise. " 'Tis nothing but a young lad! Who are you, anyway?"

"I'm Samuel Champlain. It is my father who is really captain. Old Nicholas was joking."

The daylight was increasing and the two boys inspected each other with curiosity, somewhat tinged with suspicion. Young Champlain was dressed like a sailor but his clothes were warmer and better than most. The thick blue sweater set off a fine pair of shoulders that would have looked equally well in the velvet cloak of a courtier. "Now who might you be?" demanded Sam. "A foreigner, by the way you talk."

"I'm just as French as you are — I come from St. Malo," flashed the boy. "You're the one who talks queer."

Champlain laughed. "I suppose you're right," he agreed, in the friendliest possible way. "Is that your ship, anchored out in the harbor? If you won't tell your name — then where are you bound?"

"I call myself Daniel Haye," said the boy, his face relaxing into a smile. "And me — I am bound for New France. What do you say to that?"

"I say you're lucky, and I would voyage there myself instead of to Oléron Island, down by the river mouth."

Dan's chest swelled with pride as he caught the note of envy in the other boy's voice. "They — " he gestured over his shoulder at the ship — "they in the *Swallow* are going cod fishing. It is for salt, we have come here, then we're off to the Grand Banks. But me, I shall trade with the savages on the Great River of Canada, and come back with a fortune in beaver skins."

If Samuel Champlain doubted this, he was too tactful to say so. "Have you been to New France before?" he asked.

"Oh, er — not too often," said Daniel, trying to sound very casual indeed. "But I shall manage my affair — I know all about the Great River."

"Yes?" encouraged Sam. "How many miles up river have you sailed? Is it true that, at the mouth, one cannot see from shore to shore?"

"Oh surely no river is as big as that," cried Daniel Haye. Then he looked down and began to wiggle his bare toes between two boards in the wharf. He stuck his hands into the pair of oversize sailor pants he was wearing and jingled two copper pennies — all the money he possessed. Suddenly he looked full into Sam's face, his eyes twinkling. "All right then — I've never been there — this is my first voyage."

He fully expected that Sam would turn away in disgust, but the older boy's face was even more friendly. "Spoken like an honest man," he laughed. "You're a good chap, Dan — I'd like to be going with you. You and I would find out all about that river, and the savages, too. I'd leave trading for beaver skins to you, though. I want to explore the country."

"Listen," cried Dan excitedly, "why don't you come along? We're shorthanded because no one wants to go on such a long voyage — so they'd take you."

How easy it would be! As long as Samuel Champlain could remember, he had wanted to see that fabulous New World that lay beyond the horizon. Now, at this very moment, he could make those dreams come true.

Brouage, the town where Champlain was born, was only a tiny village on the west coast of France, but it was famous for its pure white salt. Vessels from all parts of the world put in at Brouage, then weighed anchor for Spain — Puerto Rico — New France! Every time a ship set sail, Sam wished he could go with her.

"Come on — unless you're afraid," taunted the younger boy.

Champlain took a step forward, his calm disposition ruffled for the moment. "Why if you think that — take me to the mate! He'll sign me on. I'm fourteen, but I'd pass for more, and I'm strong as a man."

The boys started toward a ladder on the edge of the wharf, where a small boat was tied. Then Champlain looked down at the square box he still carried so carefully, and the light of excitement died out of his eyes. "I can't go with you, Dan," he said soberly. "I'm not ready yet."

"Well, run home then — there's plenty of time. The captain was drinking to the success of the voyage all night — he won't wake till noon. But as for me, I didn't say good-by, for fear my mother would cry, and say I'm only ten and much too young to go to sea. Better just slip off, Sam. Women are hard to handle."

All this advice amused Champlain, but he knew better than to laugh. "Look," he said, setting his square box carefully on the wharf, then unrolling the parchment he had under his arm. "This is my chart of the Brouage River, the Island of Oléron and the Strait of Maumusson. I can't go voyaging with you, Dan, because I promised my father I would finish the chart before he comes home. He's a captain in the King's Navy, and his ship will put in at Brouage any day now."

Daniel Haye looked at the big map. "Why it's — it's beautiful!" he gasped, "only I don't understand it. What are all the little numbers in the river?"

"My soundings," said Champlain proudly. "They show the depth of the channel, and I measured every one myself. Today, I go to Oléron to draw the mouth of our river as it would look to a navigator coming from La Rochelle."

"The captain of the Swallow has no chart in his locker half so fine," said Daniel. "And what's in the box? Eggs — by the way you handle it."

"No — I'll show you," laughed Sam. He turned back the lid and there, under a rather wavy piece of glass, was a quivering compass needle. The compass card was beautifully engraved, not only with the letters N, S, and so on, but with pictures of tritons and mermaids. Sam pointed to some numbers — "See, it says 1567. That's the year I was born, and Father bought this compass for me in Paris. A funny present for a baby, wasn't it? Of course I was never allowed to touch it till I was old enough to study navigation."

The two boys knelt on the wharf to watch the compass needle swing, then finally come to rest. "It's magic," breathed Dan. "Show me — where is New France from here?"

Sam took a big handkerchief out of his pocket and carefully wiped a spot on the wharf where he could spread out his chart and anchor the corners with stones. "Look at the compass, Dan, and you'll see you sail west northwest for about half a league to reach the mouth of the Brouage River. Then your course will be due north almost as far as La Rochelle."

"Why?" Dan was down on all fours puzzling over the map. "Wouldn't this way be shorter?"

"Your captain would never risk that south channel, the way the wind is now. And may the Saints protect you if you're ever caught on the Atlantic side of Oléron Island! The "Savage Coast" they call it, for 'tis but a mass of jagged rock, with here and there a sand dune or a cove almost too small for fishermen to use."

Dan got slowly to his feet. "I see why they call you captain around here," he said.

Sam closed the compass box and began to roll up the map. Then he paused and pointed to a tiny picture of a castle on the headland. "There's where I'll be today. The *Swallow* will pass close by, and I'll wave."

"So you won't come along." Dan sighed, but he knew it was useless to argue. "I must be off then. Cook sent me ashore for bread an hour ago." But the St. Malo boy lingered on the wharf to watch Samuel Champlain row down the river with long, easy strokes.

The ebbing tide carried the rowboat along, and soon the little thatched cottages of Brouage were lost among trees. A few larger houses with carved doorways and fine tile roofs could still be seen — among them, Captain Antoine Champlain's, with its walled garden, facing south. Now the

river wound among strange plots of sand, carefully dyked
and drained. These were the salt pans, where Brouage
"salt farmers" tended their queer crop. Some of the "tables"
were white with fine crystals left behind by the sea water,
others were still wet and shone like mirrors in the February sun. Old Nicholas waved to Sam, then bent to his
task, painstakingly piling salt under a little thatched drying
shed. It's going to rain, thought Sam, looking at the sky.
Old Nicholas won't like that.

The Island of Oléron was a good five miles from the
mouth of the Brouage River. A wind was rising and there
was rough water in the channel, so that Champlain had a
hard pull before his boat grated on the sandy shore. A
few minutes more, and he was comfortably ensconced on
a rocky ledge overlooking the water. Behind him rose
rugged stone battlements, and before him was a fine view
of the coast of lower Charente, or Saintonge as Champlain
called it. This was just the spot from which to complete his
chart, and Sam grinned with satisfaction. Once he was at
work time seemed to fly, and at noon he paused only long
enough to gnaw on half a loaf of bread and a hunk of cheese
he had in his pocket.

Toward late afternoon a small sailing vessel came struggling out of the Brouage River against a rising tide. It was
the *Swallow*, and Sam put aside his work to wave to Dan.
How came they to leave so late, he wondered. A moment
more, and he had something even stranger to puzzle over.
Instead of making up the coast in the lee of Oléron, the
Swallow headed for the dangerous Maumusson Strait and
the open sea!

Sam waved his cap, and from the deck of the little ship he

saw a fleck of something white. Daniel Haye was waving, too, but Sam's heart was heavy. The skipper must be a madman, he said to himself. Why, the wind had risen to half a gale!

Gathering storm clouds warned young Champlain that he should think of his own safety and head for home. But a short stretch of shore line was still unfinished on his chart. He worked feverishly in the fading light, drew one more little cove — another rock — and the chart was done.

As he clambered down from the ledge, Sam discovered that he was ravenously hungry. Babette's good soup must be simmering over the kitchen fire back home, sending up a lovely aroma of onions, garden herbs and black beans. In the small oak-paneled sitting room, Mother would be waiting, her embroidery frame before her — her eyes on the river watching for her son's boat. It was good to be going home, Sam thought.

Just then a fierce gust of wind almost tore the cap from Sam's head. The channel that separated Oléron from the mainland was a mass of tumbling green waves, tipped with white. They broke at Sam's feet with a hissing sound, while to the southwest, the deep water was suddenly pockmarked with rain.

Young Champlain paused, his hand on the gunwale of his boat. He saw the grey wall of rain rushing toward him, and he tried to gauge the force of the wind. Home was so near! It was a hard decision to make — but he knew he must stay on the island till the storm abated.

2 · THE SHIPWRECK

WITHOUT wasting any more time, Sam pulled his boat high on the beach, turned it bottom-side up and crawled under. He scooped away the layer of sand already wet with rain, and on the side away from the wind he tilted the boat just a little and propped it with a stone, to let in light and air. The precious compass and his chart, he placed in the dryest corner he could find.

If one must be marooned by a storm — who could ask for better shelter, thought Sam, as he munched on a bit of bread and cheese left over from lunch. With his hunger by no means satisfied, he tucked the last morsel of cheese and a crust of bread back in his pocket. Father always says you never can tell how long a voyage will last, he reminded himself.

Rain drummed on the floorboards overhead as Champlain eased himself into a comfortable position and went to sleep. When he awoke, it was dark and uncomfortably cold. The wind had died, but the rain was still sluicing down and an icy trickle of water had wormed its way under an oarlock. Sam fumbled around trying to dam up this unwelcome brook. Must be nearly morning, he thought. What wakened me? He found himself holding his breath to listen.

For a few moments there was no sound but the steady rapping of the rain on the overturned boat. Then, out of the darkness, came the boom of a cannon! Instantly, young Champlain was broad awake. He wriggled out from under his boat and stood listening, hardly noticing the drenching rain. Now he heard a faint confusion of voices over on the far side of the island. A boy brought up by the sea did not need to be told what had happened — a shipwreck! The Savage Coast had claimed one more victim during the storm.

Up on the ridge, a lantern was bobbing along. Someone from the fishing village had been wakened by the cannon signal of distress and was hurrying toward the sound. Sam started up the slope, then turned and dived under his boat. He drew a short sharp knife from a little leather sheath at his belt and quickly cut loose his anchor rope. How can you help drowning people without a rope, he thought, coiling it over his arm as he ran. If only he could bring his boat as well — but it was impossible to drag it so far, and to row around the point would take too long.

Over the slope Sam plunged, slipping in sand, then barking his shins on a rock in the darkness. At last he reached a cart track where the going was easier and where several fishermen with lanterns joined him. "At first I thought we were attacked by pirates," said a big man with a black beard.

"It wouldn't be the first time, eh Simon?" shouted another. "Me, I rolled out of bed and reached for my gun before I opened my eyes. Then I heard the rain on the window, and when the cannon fire came again, I knew 'twas the last night on earth for some poor devils offshore."

The cart track turned sharply to the right and twisted downward, out of sight in the dark. Far below, a single light glimmered faintly on the tiny beach which was shut in by two jagged walls of rock. Sam plunged unhesitatingly down the path, for he had mapped this very spot not long before. The first streaks of daylight were swallowed up in storm, and the sea was still a black, uneasy mass with pale breakers spilling and roaring on the sand.

Off to the left, only about two hundred yards from shore, a group of pointed rocks rose just above sea level at high tide. By daylight, they looked like the teeth of some huge monster. Sam could not see them now. He strained his eyes to look through the rain, and instead of rocks, he saw the dark shape of a vessel, her masts and spars at a crazy angle against the sky.

Already, some fishermen were trying to launch a small dory, the only boat kept in the cove. There was much confusion as men shouted to make themselves heard above the roar of the surf. "You're fools to try it," said one.

"She's breaking up fast," said another. "Hurry, can't you — give us a hand."

Sam found himself beside Simon, the big fellow with the black beard. Together, they shoved with might and main, wading waist deep into the sea before they could swing themselves aboard. "This is man's work, lad," said Simon. "Some of those landlubbers back there should have taken your place." Each pulled at a heavy oar, and when a few strokes showed that Sam's strength was equal to the task, Simon grinned in silent approval.

By now boxes, planks and broken spars were in the water all around them. One boat had succeeded in putting off from the wreck. They saw it, now high on the crest of a wave, now deep in a trough. Overloaded as it was — surely it would cover the short distance to shore. Then, even above the storm, Sam heard a terrible despairing shout. The boat rose on the next wave, keel upwards, and now there were bobbing, dark heads among the wreckage in the water.

It was impossible to save all of those who fought their way gasping to the surface, and clung to bits of plank. A man in the bow of Sam's boat stood up and took charge, telling the rowers what to do. Somehow, they would manage to come alongside a sailor, then oftener than not, the sea snatched the drowning man away before ropes or hands could reach him. Sam passed his rope up forward — it was badly needed.

Sam could not watch the rescue work. He had all he could do to handle his oar. After what seemed an age, there would be shouts of triumph up forward, a limp, wet mass would tumble into the bottom of the boat — then the dangerous job was to be done again.

All too soon, the dory was loaded, and the order came to turn back. It was growing light, but Sam wished daylight had not come after all. Men were easier to see but no easier to save, and it was agony to row away from some despairing seaman who cried "Help," though no help came. "What ship was it?" Sam asked a man who lay huddled between thwarts at his feet.

"The *Swallow*, bound for New France," the sailor answered through chattering teeth.

Of course it was the *Swallow*. Sam realized he had known it all along. No other ship had been so close to the rocky shore in the storm. Sam bent to his oar, not daring to look back at the wrecked vessel. He knew that there was no thin, blue-eyed boy among the half-drowned sailors packed into the dory. Daniel Haye had not been saved.

More people had gathered on the beach, and men waded into the waves to help pull the loaded boat ashore. Someone had managed to light a driftwood fire in spite of the rain, and the rescued seamen were helped over to the blaze. "You'll stay ashore now, young man," said Simon firmly, when Sam would have taken his seat in the boat again. "Here come fresh volunteers, and we need every ounce of strength."

Sam went over to the fire to warm himself. He was so wet with rain and spray that a motherly peasant woman thought he had been pulled out of the sea. "No," said Sam, "but I hear a few people got ashore without help. Did you see a boy among them?"

The woman shook her head. "A few were taken to the village — but all were men. A young lad would have a poor chance indeed, with such a sea running."

After what seemed an age, the dory came back with more survivors. Sam ran to help them — but there was no Daniel Haye. Finally, the boat came back with only two shipwrecked sailors, and the fishermen said it was useless to look for more. "We rowed all around the rock — as close as we dared. No living man is out there now."

"Me and my mates was lucky," a sailor from the *Swallow* said. "We struck broadside, at the height of the gale. The *Swallow*, she cracked open like an egg shell. Twelve men saved out of a crew of nineteen? That's lucky."

"Did you see a boy —" Sam began.

But the sailor interrupted impatiently. "Eh, you asked me that before. He went up the mast — captain's orders, but a fool he was to obey. The captain was drunk, I told you. No, I didn't see the boy after that."

The Oléron fishermen beached their boat, and one by one they wearily climbed the steep track. They took the shipwrecked sailors with them to share their scanty fare and get some rest. "Here's your rope, my boy," said Simon. "You'd best go along home. There's none to come from the sea now, save the dead — God rest their souls!" Champlain took the rope, but he did not leave the cove.

Now that everyone had gone, the place was very lonely. Waves broke with a hollow sound against the cliff barriers, and overhead, gulls wheeled and swooped, snatching at ship's biscuit and other provisions from the wreck. Sam noticed that a strong current swept most of the wreckage beyond the base of the southern cliff.

After a while Sam climbed the winding path. Daniel Haye must have been on the mast of the *Swallow* just as the sailor had said. He would be thrown far out into the sea, and never found. Sam paused at the top of the cliff for one last look, and from this vantage point, the course of the current was plainly seen. Why, a person would be carried down the coast about half a mile.

It was a faint hope, but Samuel Champlain was never one to give up easily. He set off toward a rocky indentation, probably formed by the very current he had just noticed. Here was no convenient cart track and sandy cove. Sam crawled to the edge of the cliff and looked down. At first he saw nothing but rocks and seaweed, and an old weather-beaten board washed ashore long ago.

Wait, though — there was a cask bobbing up and down in the backwash of the waves. The cliff was hollowed out beneath him — Sam could not quite see the water's edge. "Halloo! Halloo!" he shouted. Echoes mocked him, and only sea gulls answered his call.

Sam got to his feet. He must get home — his poor mother would be so anxious. The tide had been out, but it was turning, and it would serve to carry him up the Brouage River. Sam was just going away when a faint sound set his heart thumping. "Ho there! Help!" There was no mistaking it, someone was under the overhanging cliff.

"Courage — I come!" shouted Champlain, before he gave himself a chance to think how that might be done.

The fisherman's boat back in the cove was Sam's first

thought, but as he studied the current, he knew he could never handle the heavy boat alone. He went a little farther down the shore and saw that a weather-beaten cedar tree was clinging among the rocks. If he could get down to it — then use his rope! A few minutes more, and he stood close to the cedar on a narrow ledge. Loose stone pelted down the cliff-side into the water. It was not a spot to inspire confidence, but he could see the shore now, very well.

On a ledge lashed by the waves, even at low tide, were two huddled figures. Champlain shouted, and one of them looked up. It was Daniel Haye, and Sam shouted again, this time for joy. He quickly knotted his rope around the cedar.

The rope hung down as far as the ledge where Dan clung, but about ten feet to the left. "Can you get over there?" Sam called — for there was no other tree, nothing else to tie a rope to. Then he saw that Dan seemed to be holding his companion on the narrow ledge.

Sam swung himself over the cliff edge and climbed carefully down. It was no easy matter to find a footing near Dan, nor was there really room for a third person on that wet, seaweed-covered ledge. "What's the matter? Are you hurt?" Sam asked.

"I'm all right — " gasped Dan — "only old Pierre was thrown against the rocks. He's come to now, but when I pulled him up here he was unconscious."

Sam looked up at the cedar tree against the sky. How frail and far away it seemed! "Look, Dan, can you climb that rope?"

"Easy," said Dan.

"All right then, I'll stay and look after Pierre. You climb the cliff and when you get to the top, turn left. There's a village — you'll see smoke above the trees."

Dan got to his feet. Then a wave higher than the rest sloshed over the ledge, soaking him to the knees. The boys looked at each other in consternation. The tide was rising so fast, it would surely wash the old sailor and Sam off the ledge before Dan could possibly get help.

3 · ST. MALO – BOUND

ALL THIS time the old sailor said not a word, but sat
huddled against the cliff, watching the boys with pain-
clouded eyes. Now he spoke: "You must climb the rope,
Danny — you and your friend. Save yourselves! There's no
getting me up there, but you're young, and you can make
it."

Dan turned to Champlain, sure that the older boy would
know what to do. "Somehow I was sure you'd come," he
said. "How can we save poor old Pierre?"

Sam was thinking hard. "We might tie the rope under
his arms — if it's long enough. Then we could climb as far
as the cedar tree, brace ourselves against it and try to pull
him up. The two of us might do it."

Pierre allowed himself to be maneuvered over to the rope with many a groan. He had no broken bones, but the rocks had bruised him badly and he showed an alarming tendency to become drowsy from the heavy blow he had received on the head. Sam tied a strong bowline — with no rope to spare.

Both boys could climb well, and one after the other they swarmed up the rope, leaving Pierre hanging on the end of the line like a human codfish. Now came the hard part. "Wedge your feet against these tree roots, Dan," Champlain directed. "Keep back of me, away from the edge."

What a dead weight the old man was! At first he helped by digging his toes into the cliff when the rope swung inward. But halfway up, he seemed ready to faint. "Come on, Pierre," shouted Champlain, pretending to be angry. "Do you want to pull us both into the sea?"

Pierre set his teeth and made a final effort, raising himself hand over hand the last few feet of the way, like the old sea dog that he was. Getting him past the cedar tree to the flat cliff-top was a mad scramble, but at last they all lay panting on the grass, safe but exhausted.

A crust of bread and a morsel of cheese were still in Sam's pocket, though soggy with sea water. He divided this between his two shipwrecked sailors. "I'm not hungry, myself," he lied, hoping the Saints would forgive him.

The sun was almost overhead, and even its weak February warmth felt good. Below them, the waves dashed with a booming sound, but no one cared to look down at the ledge they had left — it was covered with swirling green water by now. "I'll find a cottage where they'll look after Pierre," suggested Champlain, who was the first to recover his breath. "Then I must be off home to Brouage in my boat. I know you're starving, Dan, but come along. Our cook's bean soup is worth waiting for."

"I'll come with you, soup or no soup," announced Dan, jumping up.

"By your leave, young man, it's Brouage for me too, if there's room in your boat," said Pierre. "I must find me another vessel bound for the Grand Banks before the season is over and the ice closes in."

The gray-headed sailor's courage pleased Champlain. "Come on," he cried. "The boat's not far, and Babette will give you a meal to make a new man of you."

Marguerite Champlain was at the wharf by the time her son's boat arrived. "There's a candle burning for you at the Shrine of St. Christopher — " she confessed — "but of course I was sure you would come soon."

Sam presented his new friends, who bowed respectfully. "A lucky thing for Danny and me, ma'am, that your son was storm-bound on the island," said Pierre.

"You must tell me all about it," said Madame Champlain, "but first, come to our house. It is just down the lane, and there's a fine dinner cooking. Babette saw the young master's boat almost as soon as I did, and she has a fat fowl roasting on the spit."

After dinner they walked in the walled garden. "Until you find a ship, Pierre, I could use someone to spade over my flower beds," said Sam's mother.

"With all my heart, ma'am," agreed Pierre. Then he

looked anxiously at the garden wall where fruit trees grew, their branches cut and trained to form a pattern. "I'm just a fisherman, you understand. I wouldn't dare touch them — them ladders."

Madame Champlain laughed. "It has taken me years to train those apples and pears. I don't expect you to know about them — though Sam is learning to be a good gardener."

Pierre could not see that gardening mixed well with seafaring, and when a Grand Banks-bound vessel came along two weeks later, he signed on and joyfully said good-by. Dan almost decided to go too, but by this time old Pierre had told the boy what life was really like aboard a Banks fishing vessel. "We'll be sixty leagues or more off Newfoundland," said Pierre. "There we'll stay, with sails down for nigh on to three months. You'll see no land, but only fog and icebergs. Each man of us will bait a hook, drop the line with a three-pound lead, then pull in a cod. Just like that, over and over."

"But isn't it exciting? Cod are big fish — don't they put up a fight?"

"About as much fight as an old boot," laughed Pierre. "And then, when the ship is swarming with slimy fish and your back is ready to break — why the work is just begun. We set up a board to make a long table on deck. One man chops off cod heads and throws them in the sea. Another cleans, and another cuts out most of the backbone. Then into the salting tub go the cod for four and twenty hours, before we pack them away in the hold. It's work, work, work, with no rest even for the Lord's Day."

In spite of Pierre's purposely gloomy picture, Dan might still have sailed for the Banks, but for one thing. "Are you sure you can't even see the shore? Don't you ever talk to savages and hunt the deer?"

Pierre laughed again. "Thirty-eight times have I crossed the old Atlantic — never have I seen the New World yet!"

Neither Samuel Champlain nor Daniel Haye understood how the old fisherman could be content with such voyages. "Dan, you ought to ship aboard a fur-trading vessel," said Champlain.

"I know — but they wouldn't take me. I — I ran away from home, you know, but if I could get back to St. Malo, I'd never go to sea again without my father's consent, and proper papers drawn up, and even advance wages given to my mother. That's how a good captain signs on a cabin boy but I didn't know that till Pierre told me."

"We must help you get home again," said Sam.

But this was not a simple problem. By land, St. Malo was about two hundred miles away, with no direct road and no means of travel for Dan, save his own two feet. By sea, the distance was more than twice as far, and who could tell when a St. Malo-bound boat would come along with room aboard for a small boy!

It was Captain Antoine Champlain, home from his cruise, who solved the problem, though not quite as Sam wished. "Father, my chart of the Brouage River is nearly perfect — you said so yourself," he began. "I think I have studied long enough now and I'm sure I could get a berth aboard a fur trader. Would you take Dan and me to St. Malo on your frigate? You know how I long to sail to the New World."

"Leave your studies to become a common seaman! No, son, that's ridiculous. You've a lot more to learn, and Father Joseph says your Latin is far from brilliant."

"But Father, what good is Latin to a seaman!" As a rule, Sam dared not question his father's decisions but this time the disappointment was too great to be borne in silence.

To his relief, his father was not angry. Instead, Captain Champlain went over to his big sea-chest and brought out a large, rather weather-stained parchment which he laid carefully upon the table. "See here, son. I found this for you at a little book-shop in Madrid. It is a copy of a map drawn by a Greek geographer by the name of Ptolemy. Why, Sam, this Ancient lived one hundred and fifty years before Christ but he knew the earth was round. He proved it — by geometry! And they tell us this fellow Columbus had a new idea!"

Sam was interested in spite of himself but also a little anxious. "Do I have to study Ptolemy in Greek, Father?"

Captain Champlain's big laugh rattled Mother's china ornaments on the mantel. "You really ought to learn Greek, but I don't think I shall insist. Come and look at the map. Old Ptolemy's Mediterranean Sea is really very good."

Sam studied the map with his father and never said another word about going on a voyage. He still felt restless and impatient with books but he saw he had much to learn.

"I have a proposition to make to you," said Captain Champlain, trying to conceal his pride and approval when he saw that Sam was really growing up. "Remember my little pinnace? I have a larger one now to carry messages between my frigate and the shore. How would you like the use of the old sailboat for the summer?"

Sam turned, surprise and pleasure lighting his face. "Oh, thank you, Father! She's a perfect one-man boat and I promise you she'll come to no harm." Then the restless look came back into Sam's eyes. "How far may I sail her, sir?"

Captain Champlain chuckled. "Not to New France I'm afraid. But come here." He spread out a chart. "I understand your young friend Daniel Haye wants to get home to St. Malo. What do you say to taking him there?"

Sam caught his breath. This would be a real voyage and no mistake. The distance was over four hundred miles along one of the most dangerous coasts of France. "It — it would mean three months and maybe more away from my books, sir!" Sam could hardly believe his good luck.

"A moment ago you were for tossing your books overboard forever," teased Sam's father. "Well, it's true that you need a rest from study. Now pay close attention till you get this whole chart by heart. I don't want you cast away on the coast of Finisterre. 'Land's End,' the name means, to be sure. Let's not make it Sam's end as well." Discussion of currents, ledges and prevailing winds followed and Sam studied hard and long. Father Joseph would have been astonished at his pupil's willingness to work — but somehow this did not seem like a lesson at all.

Marguerite Champlain wrote letters to Sam's uncle, Captain Provençal, whom Sam was going to visit in St. Malo. And Daniel bought salt from old Nicholas with money he had earned helping around the warehouse. "It would be a shame to make a long voyage without merchandise," he said. "Brouage salt fetches a fancy price back home."

They set sail at last and made La Rochelle by nightfall. Of course such good luck could not last all the way. Contrary winds kept them three days at a tiny port called St. Nazaire at the mouth of the Loire River. Sam passed the time sketching the place. A few soundings showed that big ships could not anchor and St. Nazaire would never be anything but a dot on the map — unless someone dredged out the harbor.

For several days' journey, the coastline was little different from that around Brouage. Now and then they glimpsed a castle where some nobleman managed to keep his family and followers safe from robbers by means of high, well-guarded walls. Sometimes they passed a fishermen's hamlet whose stone church was the largest building. Sam felt disappointed to sail nearly a hundred miles and see only a countryside just like his home.

Then suddenly the whole aspect of the coast changed. High cliffs and dangerous islets proclaimed the land of Brittany. North winds blew and the pinnace was forced to beat up against them with no safe harbor in sight. Young Champlain's face broke into a wide, joyful grin as he shortened sail. A great green wave broke over the bow drenching both boys. Dan began to bail frantically but the look of pure joy never left Sam's face. He was scared — yes. But how he loved it!

Just at nightfall, they found shelter in a tiny cove. "How

did you know we could put in here?" cried Dan in surprise, mingled with relief.

Sam pointed to an old ruined watchtower on an island — old even in 1581 — and to a single strange stone pointing at the sky like a finger. "Father's chart gave those landmarks," he said. "They were easier to recognize than I supposed."

Dan had been helping to beach the boat. Now he looked at the strange stone. One glance, and the boy from St. Malo turned pale with terror. "No, no," he gasped. "We can't stay here. Come away! We must launch the boat and go on."

"Nonsense," said Sam shortly, "here's where we spend the night."

But Dan was shaking with fright. "You don't understand," he pleaded. "It's the Druid Stone! A man with a long white beard will come to kill us with a knife shaped like the new moon. My mother knows. She came from a place where there are long rows of pagan stones like that and not a soul from her village would go near them at night. The priest said men called druids put the stones there by magic arts."

Now, Samuel Champlain was almost as frightened as Dan. The wind had dropped. Perhaps they could put to sea after all. Then Sam saw why a calm had fallen — fog was coming in. Devil or no devil, they were prisoners in the cove.

4 · A PARTING GIFT

SAMUEL CHAMPLAIN felt a creeping sensation along the back of his neck whenever he glanced at the tall, solitary stone. Now fog shrouded the rock until it really looked like a druid priest in long white robes. "Gather driftwood and light a fire, quick," commanded Sam, hoping his voice sounded braver than he felt.

After a supper of hot porridge, cooked over the camp-fire, both boys felt better. "Father says a good captain reads prayers aboard ship night and morning," said Sam. "I'm afraid we forgot but now's the time to start." He got out the Latin prayer book his mother had given him.

Daniel Haye could not understand the words but their familiar sound brought a reassuring picture of candles in quiet churches back home. He felt wonderfully comforted and so did Sam, who could translate the promise of security and protection in the lines he had just read. Both boys slept soundly all night.

In the morning the fog had lifted and the Druid Stone on the point was just a queer rock, not in the least terrifying. The boys set sail once more and another week brought them off the coast of Normandy. "This is my country," cried Dan joyfully. "There is none better in the world."

Champlain laughed. "To hear you talk, King Henry III of France is my king, perhaps — but not yours!"

"Let the French from Paris mind their own business and we Normans wish them well," scowled Dan, although his eyes were twinkling.

When he saw St. Malo, Sam did not laugh at Norman pride and independence. His admiration was so great that even Dan was satisfied. "What walls! What towers!" he cried. "See the sun flash from the halberds of the soldiers as they march to and fro on the battlements!" Above the fortifications, row upon row of high gabled roofs seemed trying to shoulder each other aside for a view of the sea and the forest of masts in the harbor.

The boys found a snug berth for their boat between two fishing vessels and hurried into the town before the great iron gates should close and lock them out for the night. "I'll take you to the house of your uncle," offered Dan. "I know it well for it is one of the finest in town." They walked through the darkening street till they came to a great carved oak door set in a stone wall. A servant had just placed a flaming torch in an iron ring beside this entrance. "Good-by," said Dan. "Don't let anyone show you my town but me. I'll come for you in the morning."

Next morning, true to his word, Dan was at the door and the two boys set out.

"Hurry!" urged Dan. "There's something going on at the market square. We mustn't miss it. There's a great crowd but I don't think it's a hanging because I didn't see the gallows. Maybe it's gypsies with a dancing bear —or jugglers. I love jugglers, don't you?"

"I never saw any," said Sam, for Brouage was only a small town off the beaten path and traveling entertainers never went there.

The market square was overflowing with more people than Samuel Champlain had ever seen in his life. Amid laughter and craning of necks, everyone tried to see what went on around a wooden platform in the middle of the square. A man, dressed in silk doublet and hose, a fur-lined cape and velvet cap was haranguing the crowd but nobody could hear a word he said.

With the ease of a slippery young eel, Daniel Haye threaded his way through the mob, dragging Champlain after him. In no time at all the two boys reached the edge of the wooden platform. Then they stared in amazement.

No laughing acrobats in bright-colored tights held the center of the stage. In the middle of the platform stood a man and two boys, motionless, like three bronze statues. The man's face was hideously painted with three red stripes and a green one across nose and cheeks. He wore no clothes except a sort of leather apron and his lean muscular body was a light coppery tan. The boys were dressed the same way but they had painted their faces with narrow black lines.

"Come right up. Look at the savages from Canada," bellowed the merchant in the fur-lined cloak. "This way! This way to the red men! See them dance! Hear them sing!" The man paused to prod his captives with the point of his sword.

The Indians never so much as looked at their tormentor but began a strange chant of a few notes repeated over and over. The crowd laughed but Samuel Champlain did not join in. Somehow, he did not need to be told that these were brave people singing their death song. Sam thought he had never in his life seen such unhappy faces.

Dan was laughing with the rest and Sam turned on him angrily. "It's not funny," he snapped. "Those boys are about our age. How would you like it if someone took you from your home and made sport of you before a crowd of people?"

"Just listen to that crazy song!" said Dan, defensively. "And see what a queer color they are! They're not people like us — they're nothing but savages. I dare you to pinch the big fellow, Sam. Go ahead. See what he'll do."

Sam's eyes blazed. "Let them alone," he cried. "They have feelings just like you and me, no matter what color their skins are." He turned his back on Daniel Haye and walked over to the red-faced merchant.

On seeing Sam, the merchant stopped his harangue. "Now here's a fine lusty lad wants to sign on my ship and see more of my savages," he said with false geniality.

"Mister — why don't you let those people go?" Sam demanded.

The merchant laughed. "Let them go! Why, young man, you must be off your head! If you could have seen the

trouble I had catching them you wouldn't talk so. I lured them on my ship with a promise of presents but it took four men to tie them up. They fought like tigers. I caught three boys but one contrived to jump into sea, bound as he was!"

Samuel Champlain knew it was useless to talk to this man. He turned away and as he looked at the jeering, laughing crowd a terrible wave of loneliness swept over him. Sam seemed to be the only one who felt sorry for the captive Indians. It was foolish to be so cross with Dan. Dan was no worse than the rest.

Just then he heard a voice at his elbow. "What do you say we get out of here? I — I don't like the show so well either." Dan grinned sheepishly. "I didn't pinch them. I got to thinking and it could be Daniel Haye up there, just like you said."

The two boys went off together. They stopped at Captain Provençal's house but Dan felt rather ill at ease in the big paneled room overlooking the harbor. Servants kept flitting in and out and the chairs with their velvet cushions were all too grand for comfort. Dan's home was in striking contrast. Eternally damp stone steps led to a dark room half underground, where Dan's father and mother lived with their eight children and somehow managed to be clean and self-respecting — though often hungry.

Evidently Dan had told his family all about his adventures, and Champlain was much embarrassed to find himself a hero. "I don't know how to thank you," cried Dan's mother, trying to kiss his hand.

Before many days, it was time for Champlain to start

his journey home. He called for Dan and they went to the water's edge below the city wall for a last talk together.

"I should think you would all live in the country and have a big garden," said Sam, looking a bit longingly at the green countryside beyond St. Malo.

Dan shrugged his shoulders. "Mother would never feel safe outside the city gate," he explained. "Once we had a farm but I was too little to remember it. Then came a war between two noblemen and our farm was burned. Of course we didn't really own the land, and when our over-lord was beaten in battle, the other lordship took our farm and gave it to his followers."

"Why that was wrong!" cried Sam.

But Dan only laughed. "That's the way things are. Peo-ple like us can't go to a great gentleman and tell him he's wrong, you know. I don't care. I'm going to be a sailor and my own man when I am grown." Then he added, wist-fully, "You'll be a Captain someday. I wish I could sail on your ship. I would serve no other man."

"When I finish my studies, you and I will go adventuring in New France," promised Sam. "Meanwhile, I have a pres-ent for you."

"What is it?" cried Dan, much excited. He was not used to receiving gifts.

Sam unfastened a leather sheath from his belt. "Here — how do you like your new knife?" he said with a grin.

"*My* knife!" Dan stared at the short dagger which Cham-plain had handed him. It had a sharp two-edged blade and a heavy ivory handle. On the blade was a fine tracery of leaves and flowers and the word TOLEDO in small letters.

"Why this is the knife you bought at the little shop down by the wharf. The shop-keeper said it once belonged to a Spanish pirate."

"I bought it for you — not for me," said Sam. "Don't you remember how I made sure you liked it?"

Dan held the dagger in his hand, enjoying its weight and balance. "It's going to bring me luck," he said. "I'll keep this knife always."

The boys made their way up the steep street of the town. This was good-by, though neither said so. When they reached the tiny unpaved alley where Dan lived, there were his mother and all the neighbors out in the street in a great state of excitement. "Dan, Dan, where have you been?" his mother cried.

Then she remembered her manners and made a curtsy to Champlain. "Good day to you, young sir. You must excuse me but I have great news."

She turned to her son again. "Daniel, hurry! Get on your best coat. No, your brother has a better one — wear that. Go to the wharf. Father is waiting and there's a captain who wants to sign you on as cabin boy. Hurry, dear boy, before they choose another for the place."

Sam walked quietly away smiling to himself at all the hustle and bustle. There was no danger that another boy would be taken. Uncle Provençal had been able to arrange everything. "If this Daniel Haye is half the lad you say, the place is his," promised Uncle Provençal, "and the ship is the best in St. Malo Harbor."

The adventure Sam wanted for himself, he had helped to get for his friend, but he set out for home feeling well

pleased. With good wind and good weather, he arrived
safely in Brouage once more. His books and even Father
Joseph's Latin lessons did not seem so tiresome now and
he studied hard.

It was fortunate, however, that Samuel Champlain could
not see how many years lay ahead before his own voyages
began. Just as his studies were completed and he was ready
to become a navigator, civil war broke out in France.

In 1589, Henry of Navarre became King of France because of the death of his older brother. He was a long way
from the throne, however. Henry was a Protestant and the
"Catholic League" of France, eagerly abetted by Philip of
Spain, refused to recognize a Protestant ruler.

The Spanish King sent soldiers into France and anyone
with any shrewdness could see that he hoped to snatch a
good slice of territory while the French quarreled among
themselves. The Catholic League drove Henry of Navarre
away from the vicinity of Paris, but he marched into Normandy where many cities opened their gates and proclaimed him king. He was a man after a Norman's heart
— more at home in armor than brocaded silk — brought up
among peasants instead of in a palace.

Samuel Champlain had a difficult choice to make. He
was a very earnest Catholic, yet the only leader who seemed
capable of saving France was the Protestant Henry of
Navarre. Champlain chose Prince Henry, joined his army
and soon rose to become quartermaster in charge of finding supplies and quarters for the army.

In 1598, Prince Henry was firmly established as Henry

IV, King of France. To Champlain's delight, Henry became a Catholic, but he signed the Edict of Nantes which gave freedom of religion to his country. The army in Brittany was disbanded and Samuel Champlain was free to lead his own life. He was thirty-one years old when at last he set sail on his first important voyage. Yet no man ever packed more discoveries and adventure into an active life than he.

5 · UNDER THE SPANISH FLAG

WHEN the civil wars ended, Champlain was at St. Malo at the house of his uncle Provençal. King Henry had given a safe conduct to the Spanish soldiers who had fought against him, and Captain Provençal was busy gathering together a French fleet to transport these unwelcome visitors back home. "How would you like to sail to Spain with me as mate of my flagship, the *St. Julien?*" proposed Uncle Provençal.

Champlain jumped at the chance. He had never lost his desire to see the New World and Spain was a step in the right direction. From Spain, ships sailed to South America all the time. "Help me sign up a reliable crew," said Uncle Provençal, and Sam went right to work.

St. Malo was a sailors' town and Champlain soon found men eager for adventure. I always liked these Norman French — he thought — ever since I met a boy from here, years ago. On impulse, he turned to a new member of his crew. "Ever hear of a fellow called Daniel Haye?" Sam asked.

The man's dark face flashed into a smile. "Yes, sir. He's an old shipmate of mine. He lives on the Street of the Mariners, near the Great Gate."

Sam went around to the Street of the Mariners that very evening. I told Dan we'd sail together someday, he thought. Maybe the time has come. But he found only a plump little old lady, ensconced in a pleasant room overlooking the harbor. "What a fine gentleman you have grown to be, Monsieur Champlain!" cried Dan's mother. "Indeed I remember you. You are taller, to be sure, and your shoulders, they are even more broad. But your smile is the same."

When Sam inquired after her son, the old lady looked anxious. "A Dieppe vessel put in here, short-handed, and Dan signed on," she said. "At the market, today, I heard that the *Stella* was bound for the West Indies — where Spain forbids all foreigners to go."

Champlain laughed. "Now don't look so downcast, Mother Haye. A smart chap like Dan can easily outwit those Spaniards. They have no right to all the wealth of the New World, you know. Dan will come home with his pockets full of gold."

The little old lady sighed. "That's just the way my

Danny talks. You young fellows never think how it would be if you get caught. You'd be chained to a rowers' bench in a Spanish galley."

"Even galley slaves escape," countered Sam. He tried to give Dan's mother a little present but she said all her needs were supplied because Dan had been paid a good round sum in advance for signing aboard the *Stella*.

The *St. Julien* was anchored in the harbor of Blavet, now called St. Louis, on the south coast of Brittany, near L'Orient. A small coastwise vessel carried Champlain and his St. Malo seamen to Blavet and from there they sailed for Spain on the first day of August. For ten days all went well, as they journeyed southward along the coast of France and across the Bay of Biscay. Then a great wind sprang up. It roared in the rigging and sent the *St. Julien* staggering. A moment before, she had been sailing serenely at the head of the convoy. Now all the ships were scattered like frightened pigeons in a park and the *St. Julien* bucked the seas alone.

Champlain studied his uncle's chart. It was impossible to tell exactly where the ship might be, but a bold promontory south of the Bay of Biscay seemed perilously close. Sam read the words CAPE FINISTERRE! The memory of the Druid Stone flashed into his mind with grim foreboding but he sharply reminded himself that this was Spain, not Brittany.

Wrapping a cloak around him, Sam left the cabin. "Get aloft and keep a lookout for land on the port side," he heard his uncle shout to a seaman in the lower part of the vessel. Then the wind dropped for a second and in the momentary calm Sam heard the sound of breakers. He cried out a warning but a grinding shock sent him sprawling to the deck.

Instantly all was terror and confusion aboard the *St. Julien*. Captain Provençal shouted orders from the high poop deck but he could not make himself heard above the wind and waves. Champlain picked himself up and leaped into the waist of the vessel among the men. "All hands aloft to reef sail," he ordered, in a strong and confident voice. The men forgot their panic. They began to obey eagerly.

The *St. Julien* had struck a reef but she did not sink. Down in the hold of the ship, Champlain worked with frantic haste, waist deep in water. While sailors heaved at the pumps, he nailed planks and canvas over a gaping hole in the hull. At last the patch held. "There's a man I'd

sail under from here to Kingdom Come," said one of the crew, as he watched Champlain climb wearily up the companionway to report to Captain Provençal that the *St. Julien* would float again.

A rising tide lifted the ship off the rock and she limped slowly into a harbor on the Island of Bayonna where permanent repairs could be made. One by one, the rest of the fleet appeared. They sailed on, safely reaching Cadiz, where Champlain saw the Spanish soldiers march off on Spanish soil. Now let them stay home and never invade my country again, he thought.

The French ships were paid off and sent back — all but the *St. Julien*. The Spanish general liked this vessel so much that he chartered her and sent her to San Lucar, the port of Seville.

To Champlain's disappointment, the *St. Julien* tied up at San Lucar with nothing to do except await orders that never seemed to come. Sam bought himself some fine parchment, pens, brushes and paints. Soon he completed a chart of San Lucar Harbor with all soundings carefully recorded. Next, he journeyed up river to Seville, fifty miles away, and sketched the fortifications.

Sam was sitting on the deck of the *St. Julien*, peacefully drawing, one morning, when he heard a great commotion along the wharves. At first he did not look up. Fights were always breaking out among the rough river-front crowd, with much yelling and calling of names. Then a word or two caught his attention. "The English! The dogs of English are out!"

Sam got up and walked over to the rail. Tied alongside

the *St. Julien* was a fast sailing vessel called an "advice boat." She was just in from the Azores. "The English are headed for Puerto Rico," said a sailor from this boat, in answer to Sam's shouted question.

Champlain felt a thrill of excitement. The *St. Julien* was well-armed and she was in the service of Spain. A sea battle would just suit the adventurous French mate, after all these weeks of idleness. Sure enough, the King of Spain ordered twenty vessels and two thousand men to the rescue of his rich West Indies colony. And the *St. Julien* was among those chosen to go on the expedition.

What activity there was aboard ship now! Champlain drove the Spaniards at San Lucar nearly crazy by insisting that ammunition and supplies be delivered at once and not "*mañana.*" "Puerto Rico is in danger now — not tomorrow," he told them. "Wake up! Get to work!"

Before long, the *St. Julien* was ready to put to sea. The other vessels were not, however, and now the Spanish captains laughed behind the energetic Frenchman's back. Champlain could do nothing but wait.

Then one day the Spaniards stopped laughing. Another advice boat came in with grim news. Puerto Rico had been taken, looted and was now held for ransom by a handful of English privateers! Much to Champlain's astonishment, the King of Spain meekly paid the ransom and called off the expedition.

Sam went to the beautiful Moorish palace of the governor of Seville. Many Spanish grandees were there, among them, Don Francisco Colonna, Knight of Malta. "I need fast, well-armed fighting ships for convoy duty in New

Spain," said Don Colonna. "These thieving English grow bolder every day and we must guard our treasure ships as never before."

Champlain bowed from the waist in a slightly mocking imitation of a Spanish gentleman. "May I suggest that the *St. Julien* is a fine ship?" he said. "She is munitioned and ready to sail at a moment's notice."

Uncle Provençal had recently become Pilot General to the King of Spain. He added a good word or two about the ship and especially about his nephew's ability as a navigator. A few days later, Samuel Champlain stood on the high poop deck of the *St. Julien* — captain of his own vessel for the first time!

"You deserve your good fortune, my boy," said Sam's uncle, when he came aboard the *St. Julien* to say good-by. He caught sight of some papers on the table in the new captain's cabin. "What's this — your last will and testament?" he laughed.

"No, Uncle, just some — well some rules I've been setting down for myself," Champlain replied.

Without so much as by your leave, Captain Provençal picked up the papers and began to read. "A good ship-master is robust and alert, so that whatever happens he may appear on deck, and in a loud voice, issue orders to the crew. Occasionally, he should not disdain to lend a hand."

Captain Provençal nodded approvingly. "You have here a portrait of yourself — even as mate." He went on reading. "A captain should have his own private compass and often refer to it to know if the course is properly kept." And there on the table was Sam's beautiful compass — the one his father had given him — on his own ship at last.

"Good-by, my boy," said Captain Provençal. " 'Aid thyself and God will aid thee.' I see you know the proverb well."

The *St. Julien* sailed away from San Lucar on the first day of January, 1599. "With a very steady, cutting wind — " as Sam put it — they reached the Canary Islands in six days. But more than two months passed before they sailed into Puerto Rico.

What a scene of desolation they found! Not a house in the little settlement was standing. Twelve ships had been captured, loaded to the gunwales with sugar, hides, ginger, gold and silver, and then carried off to England. Don Colonna groaned. But when he learned that the fort had been stripped of fifty brass cannon, his language made even the sailors gasp.

Champlain talked to the inhabitants of the town who came straggling out of the woods where they had hidden. "With such a strong fort, how came the settlement to be taken?" he asked.

The Spanish garrison were loud in their excuses. Those cursed English came in such small ships that they were able to anchor in a shallow, unguarded cove. They attacked overland while all the guns of the fort pointed seaward. And if the guards on the land side of the fort slept soundly, who could blame them? An enemy attack by land! It was an outrage.

Sam suppressed a smile. He wondered if the English had sunk so low as to attack during siesta, when every good

Spaniard must have his afternoon nap. Since no one seemed to object, he made a careful map of Puerto Rico and the harbor defenses. Then, just for fun, he drew a picture of a huge chameleon which he saw sunning itself on a log. The picture was handsome, all painted in bright colors.

Haiti was the next port of call. All foreign ships were forbidden to go near this island and the enslaved natives were given their freedom if they reported a vessel with any flag save the red and gold of Spain. Don Colonna was told that two French trading vessels had recently been seen along the coast.

Off went the Spanish Don and, just at nightfall a few days later, he came upon a tiny cove. There lay two ships, hardly bigger than fishing boats, and all around them clustered native canoes. "We've caught the thieving traders red-handed," exulted Don Colonna. He signaled the *St. Julien* to help block the mouth of the cove.

Sick at heart, Sam watched the French traders frantically trying to get up sail. It was no use. They were trapped, and they knew it. Now, one crew hastily abandoned ship and rowed for the shore. "After them!" shouted Don Colonna. "We need galley slaves." The Spaniards put over a longboat.

It looked as if the captain of the other trading vessel had completely lost his head. He set his sails but when he saw that escape was cut off, he ran his vessel full speed into a reef. "The fools!" roared Don Colonna. "We've lost a good ship!"

But Champlain watched the French crew jump into a boat and row smartly ashore. They beached their skiff hardly a boat's length ahead of Don Colonna's men but they disappeared into the jungle with no evidence of panic. Sam's eyes gleamed with pride. That wreck was no accident! The traders had deliberately sacrificed their ship to keep her out of Spanish hands.

Sam picked up a spyglass to see if he could make out the name of the French ship before she sank. "*Stella*," he read. "*Stella* – Dieppe." His face grew grim as a picture flashed into his mind – a picture of a little old lady back in St. Malo, waiting for her son to come home. There was nothing he could do, save breathe a prayer for Daniel Haye, hiding over there, in the jungle!

6 · A PEN AND A SWORD

THE FOLLOWING day, the Spaniards found thirteen traders
at the port of St. Nicholas. Don Colonna ordered his fleet
to line up across the bay. Then he called a council of captains aboard his flagship. To Champlain's amazement, this
meeting lasted for hours, while each captain made long
boastful speeches about what he would do to the enemy.
In the end it was decided to do nothing — till tomorrow!

Aboard the French, English and Flemish traders caught
in the bay, there was great activity — as Sam noticed when
he left the council meeting. He mustered out his own
men. "We are going to see some action," he told them.
"Gunners, to your stations. Caulkers and carpenters, place

water casks about the decks for putting out fires. Then
stand by to repair damage."

On the Spanish ships next to the *St. Julien*, the sailors
began to laugh and jeer at Champlain's men. "Look who's
playing soldier!" they shouted. "Do you think those toy
sailboats in there will dare to fight? There won't be any
shooting."

Just at dawn next day, the toy sailboats struck. Following a carefully worked-out plan, the English charged the
center of the line of Spanish ships. The French and Flemish took the flanks. Head on they came, their small guns
pouring a stream of shot into the towering Spanish hulls.
Only one ship was ready to return their fire — it was the
St. Julien.

The surprise was so complete that Don Colonna ordered
his anchor ropes cut at the hawse-holes so he could get
away! The brave little traders promptly sailed through
this breach in the line. As the smoke cleared, only one
solitary trading ship was to be seen, sailing up and down
among the Spaniards in a queer, irresolute sort of way.

Seeing one very small enemy vessel, Don Colonna took
courage and managed to bring his great clumsy galleon
about so as to have a shot at her. He missed. When the
black powder-smoke cleared away, there was the little pinnace, impudently sailing, now to port, now to starboard.
The admiral himself hailed her, calling on her to surrender.
There was no reply.

"Lower a boat. Boarders away!" shouted Don Colonna.

Nobody moved. At last one white-faced sailor spoke.
"Only look, my lord! That ship is steered by the Evil One

and sailed by blackest magic! Not a man is to be seen on her decks!"

Don Colonna whipped out his sword and forced his men into boats. In fear and trembling they climbed aboard the pinnace and now the mystery was solved. The little ship was empty! Her tiller was lashed and her sails set. She had been set adrift to confuse the enemy and in this she succeeded admirably.

Considerably delayed, the Spanish fleet set off after the traders. But the little vessels cracked on all sail in their race for life. Gradually, the heavy galleons were left behind and at nightfall Don Colonna gave up the chase.

Champlain was delighted at the escape of his countrymen. At the same time he was exasperated with the Spaniards. "Our admiral had better ships, more men and more munitions of war," he wrote in his journal. "The traders were only saved through the cowardice of the Spaniards."

Leaving the islands of the West Indies, the Spanish fleet sailed along the Peninsula of Yucatan and came at last to San Juan de Luz. This mighty island fortress was a port of call in New Spain for all the king's treasure ships. It was famous throughout the world for the vast wealth that lay within its walls, yet Samuel Champlain was probably the first Frenchman ever to walk freely about the island.

Sheer walls rose straight from the sea. Here and there, great bronze rings were set in the masonry and the *St. Julien* tied up to a ring, finding barely room between two cargo ships. All day long, Champlain saw slaves carrying bars of gold and silver into those ships. This loading will take a long time, Sam thought. He got permission to leave the *St. Julien* and go to Mexico City.

A road, built by slaves, led inland for about two hundred and fifty miles. Champlain was prepared to find a handful of native huts and perhaps a stone fort at the end of his journey. Instead, he saw temples, churches and palaces, lining well–laid-out streets. There were shops, bulging with rich wares. About fifteen thousand Spaniards and six times as many Indians thronged this great city, which was built on an island in a lake. Sam got out his paints and drew one of his best pictures, showing the island, the causeway and the crowded buildings in this strange town.

Gold and silver circulated among the Spanish of Mexico City but the Indians paid for their simple needs with cocoa beans. Sam was delighted with this native money. He found he could buy a day's supply of food for himself and his servants for five or six beans. Then, after marketing was over, he could have his cocoa bean "change" ground up and steeped in water, to drink. "Cocoa is excellent," wrote Champlain in his journal. "The natives drink it in the morning, as our sailors take brandy. They can go all day without eating and not feel very hungry."

After spending a month in Mexico City, Sam reported back to his ship. All was well aboard the *St. Julien* but she was to stay a while longer at San Juan de Luz. Once more, Sam got permission to travel and this time he took passage on a small ship bound for Panama.

The Isthmus of Panama seemed to Champlain like a locked gate, barring the way to India. "A passage might be made from the South Sea to that on this side," he wrote in his journal. "The route would then be shortened by more than fifteen hundred leagues." Three hundred years passed before Champlain's vision became a reality in the Panama Canal!

In Champlain's day, long voyages were the general rule and now Sam had been away from home for two years. He was glad when orders came to proceed to Havana, Cuba, with the galleons from San Juan de Luz. But the *St. Julien* lay at anchor at Havana for four months more, while galleon after galleon joined the homeward-bound fleet, from all parts of New Spain. What fabulous wealth lay packed away in those clumsy wooden vessels! No wonder the Spanish were constantly at work to improve the fortifications for their fine harbor at Havana. No wonder the *St. Julien* and every other available man-of-war assembled to convoy the Spanish gold across the sea.

The day of departure arrived at last. Bells rang out, while dignitaries of the church filed in solemn procession to the wharves to bless the out-going fleet. Pale candles flickered in the brilliant sunshine and the sharp scent of incense mingled with the perfume of flowers. From the fort, the cannon boomed in salute as the galleons moved majestically out to sea.

"Stay together, whatever happens," commanded the admiral, nervously. And the *St. Julien*, being a fast sailer, briskly circled the treasure ships like an intelligent collie rounding up sheep. All went well until they were six days out of sight of land. Then a tempest struck.

Aboard the *St. Julien*, Champlain had been watching the weather with an anxious eye. He saw black clouds boiling up out of the east and his ship was already close-reefed when the wind came. With the galleons, it was a different matter. A few of the more alert captains had men aloft, taking in sail. The majority wallowed complacently along like fat old women coming home from market. Crack went their sails, like the report of a cannon! Many were dismasted during the first three minutes of the gale.

Now the rain came down like a black curtain over sea and sky. Sam saw nothing more of the laboring galleons as his ship fled down the wind. There was no use setting a course. The thing to do was to stay afloat if that were humanly possible. The *St. Julien* heeled over and tore along like a runaway race-horse.

All night, Champlain stayed on deck watching over his ship. He was proud of the gallant way she rode out this storm. When the sky cleared they were miles off course but they were safe. Sam searched the horizon with his spyglass. Not a Spanish ship was to be found!

The *St. Julien* cruised about for a week, keeping in the general direction of the Azores. At last, Champlain managed to round up two cargo vessels with very nervous captains. "Stay close to us!" they implored. "Suppose those dogs of English should spot us now!" In their opinion, the rest of the fleet was surely lost.

Champlain got his two charges safely to the Azores in spite of their fears. They cast anchor and waited a week. Then, one by one, the other galleons came struggling along. As though by a miracle, every ship in the convoy finally arrived and once more they all set out for Spain. This time, luck was with them. The weather was good and, best of all, they sighted two small English ships, fitted out for war.

Boom roared the cannon as the whole convoy swooped down. Who could be braver than the Spaniards — with such odds in their favor! The two ships were captured and taken to Seville. Don Colonna was very much pleased with himself for now nothing need be said about the thirteen trading vessels that got away.

When this voyage was over, no offer the Spanish could make could tempt Champlain to remain in their service. The next important step in his career was already planned. He would take service under his own flag and set sail next time for New France.

The first move would be to go to the French king's court. At court, appearances count heavily, Sam said to himself, so he laid out some money in fine Spanish merchandise. First, he chose a sword made by the famous Toledo craftsmen. Although the hilt was inlaid with gold, it was a real weapon and not a toy such as most courtiers affected. Boots of Cordova leather also came from Spain and Sam had a pair made to order. He bought lengths of velvet, dyed deep crimson by a secret Spanish process.

Once arrived in Paris, Champlain spent a week or two renewing old acquaintances. An obscure young sea captain would be foolish to present himself at court without a sponsor and Sam needed to find some friend who might have influence with the king. He neglected nothing that could help his dreams to come true.

One day, a tall white-haired gentleman appeared in

Paris and Champlain knew he had found his man. He hastened to pay his respects to Aymar de Chastes, his former commander in the wars. This fine old soldier was a man of highest integrity. As Champlain put it, "The king loved him especially." And Henry IV was clever, for he had made De Chastes Governor of Dieppe, knowing that no foreign enemy would ever enter that seaport, no insurrection raise its head, while the brave commander stood guard.

"I suppose your royal honors have forced you to give up voyaging," suggested Champlain, when he called on his old friend. Sam remembered talks over the camp-fire, in his soldiering days, when he and the commander had both confessed to a longing to see the New World.

"Not at all," smiled De Chastes. "In 1600, His Majesty gave me permission to leave Dieppe for a short time and I founded a trading station at a place called Tadoussac, on the St. Lawrence River in Canada."

Champlain's eyes lighted with enthusiasm. "I wish I could have been with you, sir."

"The voyage you have just completed was more important," said the Sieur de Chastes.

"If my experience could be of service to the king — " began Champlain.

"I was hoping you would say that," interrupted De Chastes. "You will find that Henry IV does not forget those who helped put him on his throne. These maps and writings of yours will prove that you can handle a pen as well as a sword. Come with me to court without delay!"

An appointment was made and Champlain set out by the side of this fine old nobleman who had long been his friend. Captain Champlain had no title and no lands. But the sword at his side and the manuscript under his arm were to make his fortune.

7 · ROYAL GEOGRAPHER

"The Sieur Commander de Chastes, Governor of Dieppe," announced a lackey. Then he glanced superciliously at Champlain before adding, "er — and friend." Gilded doors opened upon a long gallery which had just been added to the old palace of the Louvre. Laughter and talking stopped for a moment in the crowded room, then resumed, louder than ever.

Youths in bright-colored silks and satins fluttered about, complimenting the ladies, then pausing before a mirror to admire themselves. The court ladies received all attentions with equal indifference, for their faces were so heavily painted and powdered that a genuine smile could never have emerged from behind the mask. Over in an alcove, some Italian followers of the new queen, Marie de Medicis, whispered in their own language, while British emissaries of the ageing Queen Elizabeth eyed them with suspicion.

Through this idle crowd of hangers-on, strode the Sieur de Chastes and Champlain. Courtiers made way for the old soldier, knowing that he was high in the king's favor. "His Majesty will see you, now," said the king's secretary to the newcomers — and they entered a small room where a middle-aged man was sitting alone by the fire.

The months he had spent among Spanish grandees stood Champlain in good stead. He dropped to one knee and kissed the king's hand as if he had lived among royalty all his life.

"Where have you been, Champlain?" asked the king. "Your fellow officers came to me long ago for their reward." There was a sardonic twinkle in his eyes but also so much genuine friendliness that Sam decided not to bother with the formal speech he had prepared.

"I have been voyaging to New Spain, Sire," he said. "Here are certain maps and writings which I have the honor to present to you." Champlain opened the portfolio that he was carrying and handed the king some of his sketches.

Henry's keen mind grasped the value of Champlain's work at a glance. "Fortifications at Puerto Rico! Fortress at San Juan de Luz! Why man, you have laid bare all the most carefully guarded secrets of New Spain!" he cried.

Soon the long table in the king's private apartment was strewn with maps and drawings. "Soundings for all harbors!" marveled the king. "Elevations — distances. What a cartographer you have become!" Then King Henry IV glanced over Champlain's account of the gold and silver that poured into Spanish galleons and his brow clouded. "Think of that revenue!" he muttered. "My royal cousin of Spain could buy me out a dozen times."

Here was the opening the Sieur de Chastes had been looking for. "I have come to talk of adding similar riches to the crown of France," he said. "Consider your possessions in Canada, Sire. At present they do not produce gold but the fur trade would be a gold mine — if properly handled. The merchants of Dieppe have sent me to ask Your Majesty for exclusive rights to this trade."

As a prince, fighting for his throne, Henry of Navarre had been desperately in need of money. Now, as king, he was intensely greedy for gold. "A monopoly on the Canadian fur trade would cost your town a good round sum," he told De Chastes.

"My merchants can pay," the commander assured him.

The king laughed shortly. "If I give you this monopoly, the people of La Rochelle will be ready to cut my heart out. But Dieppe is rich."

There came a discreet knock at the door. "The ambassador from the Court of St. James is waiting," said the king's secretary. "He says he is the bearer of an important letter."

Henry IV scowled. "Tell him to come back tomorrow.

Tell him if the letter is not civil, I'll slap his face again — the way I did last time."

As the secretary made for the door, the king added: "Come back here afterwards, will you." He turned to Champlain. "What do you get out of this monopoly — supposing I grant it?"

"Sire, I have no lands — no wealth to invest."

The king tapped a map which he was holding. "You have eyes and a brain. I notice you have a sword also, which I warrant you can use. Let me see — you are a captain in the Spanish navy?"

"Captain no longer, Sire. I resigned my commission."

The secretary re-entered the room softly. "Here, Boullé — write me some papers," said Henry. "First — Samuel Champlain is to hold a commission as captain in the French navy."

While the secretary's quill was busily scratching, the king talked further with Champlain. He picked up Sam's account of the Spanish sea fight with the traders and chuckled. "I'll give you a man-of-war, and a better one than the *St. Julien* ever was," he suggested.

Champlain thanked the king for this fine offer. He took his courage in his hands when he went on to say, "Sire, it is my desire to explore the lands of New France, rather than to command a ship — if it please Your Majesty! No man knows the extent of your kingdom of New France, but someday French colonists like those of Spain should make Your Majesty rich and your people prosperous."

Crafty and unscrupulous Henry IV might be, but he was also ? statesman. "Samuel Champlain, I appoint you my Royal Geographer," he said. "I commission you to go to my territories of New France, there to prepare maps and explore the country as much as you are able. The trading company is to give you every assistance — ships, men — whatever you need. Is that clear, De Chastes? These are conditions of the monopoly. You will aid Champlain."

"With all my heart, Sire," cried the Sieur de Chastes, delighted at the favorable turn of affairs, both for himself and his protegé.

While the king's secretary was getting everything down in writing, Champlain endeavored to thank His Majesty. No other task could have been so exactly according to his heart's desire. The king smiled quizzically. "Wait — I am not done. My personal representative should be equal in rank to his associates. Hereafter you shall be known as 'The Sieur de Champlain' and a yearly income goes with the title. Thank me for that, if you will! I have not forgotten the days when I was a prince without a penny. Get yourself a servant or two — arms and equipment."

The royal audience was over but Champlain was summoned to the palace more than once after that, to confer with the king. "The Sieur de Champlain, Royal Geographer," announced the now obsequious lackey. It was surprising how many courtiers would have cultivated Sam's acquaintance these days. But unless they were seriously interested in New France, the Sieur de Champlain was too busy to bother with them.

The king drove a hard bargain before he actually gave De Chastes the exclusive right to all the furs in Canada. Not even the rich merchants of Dieppe had enough money and they were obliged to allow a few St. Malo men to buy shares in their company. A nobleman by the name of Francis Gravé, Sieur du Pont, paid heavily to join. Pontgravé, as the Sieur du Pont was called, had been to New France in 1600, helping De Chastes establish the trading post at Tadoussac and he knew he could make a profit even after the king's exorbitant demands had been met.

Champlain did not need to buy shares in the fur company or even to pay his passage to New France. The king's secretary gave him a letter ordering Pontgravé to receive the Royal Geographer. "Thus dispatched, I left Paris and sailed in Pontgravé's ship in 1603," said Sam.

He would have liked to go to St. Malo to see his friends. Did Daniel Haye ever come back from his voyage aboard the ill-fated *Stella?* Sam could not know. The king's orders took him to Honfleur, on the River Seine. In those days, Honfleur was the port of Paris. It was a busy place, crowded with sailing ships from other lands. Now it is just a forgotten town with a crumbling old castle, and Le Havre is the important channel port.

Champlain was delighted to find two Indians aboard Pontgravé's vessel at Honfleur. He still remembered the unhappy captives he had seen long ago in St. Malo. They had died after a few months of misery. But these savages had come to France of their own free will, three years before, with the Sieur du Pont. They had learned to speak French after a fashion, and now Pontgravé was taking them home, just as he had promised.

The savages found Champlain eager to learn about the country around Tadoussac. They told him all they could, drawing crude maps for him in charcoal. "We will show you," they promised. And they were pleased when this Frenchman tried to learn their language. Before the voyage was over, Champlain could exchange friendly greetings in the tongue of the Tadoussac Indians, and he knew the names of rivers he had yet to see.

On the second of May, after three months without sight of land or any other ship, suddenly they were surrounded by sea birds! They were off the Grand Banks, and they furled their sails to fish, for fresh food was scarce by now. Champlain thought of old Pierre, the Banks fisherman who must be dead these many years. Think of spending a lifetime sailing to the New World, as Pierre had done, yet never seeing it! Good as the fresh cod tasted, Sam was eager to sail on.

A few days later, Champlain paced the deck. A fog had come down — masts and rigging disappeared in mist as he gazed aloft. The dripping deck was silent and lonely. Then faintly, out of nowhere, came a sound Champlain knew well — the dashing of waves on a rocky shore. A second later and the lookout heard it too. Orders were shouted, sailors ran to the ropes and the ship came about — putting out to sea and safety. Champlain sighed as he crawled into his bunk that night. The New World still lay shrouded in mystery.

Next morning when he climbed on deck, the sky was miraculously clear. There, dead ahead, was a rocky point, Cape St. Mary, on the south coast of Newfoundland.

But even on the fifteenth of May, great ice flows barred the way to Canada. This was a different land indeed from the sunny coast of South America, yet Champlain's heart lifted with a surge of happiness when he saw the deep blue St. Lawrence River. The clear air with its scent of pines made him feel like shouting for joy. From the high shores of the Gaspé Peninsula, forests stretched as far as the eye could reach. Mountains in the distance seemed to challenge the explorer to climb their slopes and view the huge, breathtaking wilderness.

They were in the St. Lawrence River now, but to Champlain it looked more like an inland sea. Back in Paris, Tadoussac, the trading post, was spoken of as at the mouth of the River of Canada; yet, they sailed 195 miles upstream to reach it.

The country grew more beautiful as they advanced inland. How fertile the land must be, to produce such great forests, thought Champlain. There were men and women back home in France without so much as a square foot of ground to call their own. If they could come here — just think of the land they could have for the taking! Mapping and charting must come first, but Champlain was beginning to think seriously about colonies.

Tadoussac was a disappointment. A long barnlike building had been built on a rocky strip of land swept by icy winds, even during the last of May. Near by, the Saguenay poured its waters out of the north in a series of fierce rapids none but an Indian could navigate. "Why build an outpost here, when we have passed so many lovely spots?" Sam asked.

Pontgravé indicated the Saguenay. "Indians of the North bring some of the best pelts down this river. Besides — "

he shrugged his shoulders — "who cares whether the place is beautiful or not? No one lives here, and the fur trade is what matters."

Champlain worked away at drawing the location of the post, but if ever he had the choosing of a site for a town, he privately vowed he would do better.

The next day Pontgravé and Champlain had themselves rowed three miles up the St. Lawrence to a beautiful grassy point. Behind this natural meadow, pines and birches covered the steep slopes of a little hill, which was perfectly flat on top. Here, was another curious little meadow about three miles long. The formation of this point was so odd it could be recognized a long way off.

All around were barren rocky hills like those at Tadoussac, and Champlain saw at once that this was the one good site for a town. The spot, however, was already taken. About a thousand savages were living in birch-bark huts on this point of land!

8 · A SAVAGE FEAST

IT WAS the twenty-seventh of May. New grass covered the meadow on the St. Lawrence where the Indians were encamped. On the slopes of the hill behind them, birch trees were putting forth tender leaves which shone like jewels against the somber pines and cedars. The French sailors beached the skiff, and Champlain sprang ashore.

Sam had hardly landed before he was surrounded by a crowd of savages. They were in gala attire, although to European eyes, they seemed hardly dressed at all. Some wore a sort of leather apron, others a short kilt of bearskin or fox fur, while only a few had leather leggings trimmed with fringe. What they lacked in clothes, they made up in ornament. Each warrior wore several bands of leather around his neck, beautifully embroidered with shells, and at least one necklace of bears' claws. In their long black hair were eagles' feathers. Their hair was stiff with bear grease, and their bodies shone with this same rancid fat. The smell of grease was very strong indeed, and Sam gasped for breath.

"Are all your tribes as big as this one?" he asked, turning to one of the Indians who had been on Pontgravé's ship. The crowd was thickening every minute.

"Oh no," exclaimed the interpreter. "Can't you see — there are three tribes here! Some are the Montagnais, like that man over there. His face is painted with the marks of his tribe. They live here on the Saguenay River. Then there are the Ottawas, like that man with three eagles' feathers in his hair. Many eagles' feathers mean many battles. He is a great warrior from afar up the River of Canada, and beyond. And look — here comes an Etechemin." The interpreter gestured to the south, trying to tell Champlain that this tribe came from the country around what is now the Penobscot River in Maine.

"I must learn to recognize each tribe," said Sam. Under the fierce, warlike paint, he saw that these Indians were smiling and friendly. The effect was grotesque — as though they laughed and scowled at the same time. "The warriors are very happy. Is it because the hunting season is over and they have brought their furs to trade with us?" Champlain asked.

The Indian interpreter looked faintly scornful. "It is because they have been on the warpath and have taken many scalps," he said. "Today there is a great *Tabagie*. But come! The white men are invited."

"*Tabagie?*" questioned Sam.

"Yes, yes — you will see."

The crowd opened while Champlain, Pontgravé and the captain of the trading vessel were led to a bark cabin in the middle of the village. This was about three times as long as the other cabins, but no wider.

Sam stooped to enter the low door. If the smell of bear grease had been strong out of doors, in the long house it was terrific. Down the center, eight or ten kettles were bubbling over wood fires. The smoke was supposed to escape through a small square hole in the roof, but most of it filled the room. Sam's eyes were smarting as he seated himself on the ground near the far end of the cabin.

About a hundred braves sat in perfect silence, watching the kettles boil. As his eyes became accustomed to the murky darkness, Sam saw that he was sitting near a great chief or "sagamore." Many eagles' feathers in this Indian's hair marked him for a man who had seen years of warfare, while several heavy necklaces of bears' claws showed he was a great hunter. There was something hanging from the wall of the hut close behind the chief, and Champlain felt a queer shiver along his spine as he recognized human hair dangling from a bit of skin.

As Champlain ran his eye down the row of guests at the savage feast, he saw that every man had an enemy scalp or two hanging on the wall behind him. There must have been well over a hundred scalps in all so this was indeed a great celebration.

But now, at a nod from the chief, the Indian interpreter beside Champlain arose. He began to tell about his travels and adventures in France. The long speech was received in absolute silence. At the end the Indian said, "The King of France wishes you well. He wishes to people this country, and he wants you to make friends with your enemies."

The great chief sprang up. Through the interpreter, Champlain learned that peace would be impossible. A fierce tribe called the Iroquois lived in fine hunting grounds to the south and west of the St. Lawrence River. They had driven all other tribes farther and farther north, where winters were long and food was scarce. Now they threatened to take even the St. Lawrence from these Indians, who had once roamed the fertile valleys of what is now New York State. The Ottawas, the Penobscots and the mountain tribes from the Saguenay must make a stand, or perish.

Champlain felt his heart warm toward these hard-pressed people. The battle had been going on for fifty years, he learned. The Iroquois had been winning all the time, seizing more and more land from weaker tribes. Samuel Champlain could not help siding with the weak against the strong. "I will help the St. Lawrence Indians," he promised, little realizing how many hard battles lay ahead.

Now the chief took some powdery brown leaves from a pouch. He filled a small, carved bowl at the end of a long tube, and touched a live coal to it. While Sam watched closely, the chief sucked the tube, then blew smoke from his mouth. A few puffs on the ceremonial pipe, and it was handed to another chief — then to another.

Only sagamores smoked the pipe, and Pontgravé and Champlain were considered as white chiefs. They called this feast a *Tabagie*, remembered Champlain, and that is why the dried leaves they smoke are called tobacco. He had seen it in New Spain and once or twice in France, but it was far from common. Sam never learned to like tobacco very well, but he smoked many a ceremonial pipe, gravely and with dignity.

After the speeches, birch-bark bowls were filled with meat from the kettles, and passed around. There were moose meat, bear, seal and beaver. The moose tasted rather like beef, Sam said — and seal reminded him of fresh pork. Although the meat tasted good, Sam almost lost his appetite when he saw the Indians' manners. "They feed very filthy," is the way he put it. With their hands, they dipped into the bark bowls and pulled out chunks of meat. Each man had a dog lying near him, and when the warrior's hands got too greasy, he just reached out and wiped them on the dog. Sometimes they wiped their hands on their hair.

"But you couldn't blame them," said Sam, always ready to excuse his savage friends. "They have no handkerchiefs and no napkins."

Ceremonial dances followed the feast. Champlain had never seen such a sight before, and he knew that the people back home would like to hear about it. "There were one or two who sang, keeping time to the beat with their hands, which they strike upon their knees," he wrote. The tune was monotonous — more like a chant than a song. And as for the dancing — "They go not out of one place when they dance but first lift up one foot and then another, stamping upon the ground."

Champlain and Pontgravé spent the night at the Indian

town. Early next morning the chief summoned the tribes. At his signal, women dismantled the huts. Then every man loaded his belongings, his wife and children and all his furs into a canoe. Sam thought he must be dreaming. One moment, he was standing in the midst of a populous town; then it was gone!

Canoes intrigued and delighted Champlain. He examined one, and praised the workmanship in that generous way of his that won the hearts of the Indians. "They are made of the bark of trees called birch," he said, "and strengthened within by little circles of wood strongly and neatly fashioned. They are so light that a man may carry one easily, yet they will support the weight of about a thousand pounds."

Two hundred canoes took to the water and went flashing down the stream like a school of silvery salmon. Champlain jumped into his skiff and ordered his five men to row for Tadoussac. The sailors bent lustily to the oars, determined to show these savages how a boat should skim along. Without apparent effort, Indian after Indian passed them. Now all the canoes were far in the lead, and the clumsy wooden boat came in last, no matter how hard the sailors rowed.

"We should travel in canoes," said Sam.

But Pontgravé looked at him in horror. "You won't get me into one of those flimsy things," he insisted. "They tip over if you so much as turn your head."

While Pontgravé was busy examining pelts and bargaining for them with knives and beads, Champlain set out to explore the Saguenay. He found the country barren and forbidding. Fierce rapids barred his path, and he was obliged to leave his skiff and scramble along the river-bank. Once he heard the high, sweet note of a white-throated sparrow above the sullen roar of the rapids. He realized that he had seen neither bird nor animal for days.

"Does the Saguenay lead to a northwest passage to India?" Pontgravé asked eagerly, when Champlain returned. This was a common belief.

"It does not," said Champlain positively. "It leads only to a land of ice and snow."

The Royal Geographer asked for a sailing skiff and some men, so he could explore the St. Lawrence. Pontgravé was under the king's command to provide these, and since his trading was finished, he went along.

This time, Champlain found a very different river from the icy Saguenay. The St. Lawrence bore southward and at every mile the trees seemed greener, the meadows more fertile. They came to a large island and beyond the river narrowed. On the right, gray cliffs rose majestically, and at their summit was a broad plain. Champlain felt a strange thrill of pleasure. "What is this place?" he asked his French-speaking guide.

"Quebec," said the savage. "Place of Narrow Water."

"A few cannon on top of that cliff could command the entire river," Champlain declared. "It is a natural fort!"

They anchored for the night and Sam went ashore carrying a spade. Yes, the earth was rich and good. There were wild strawberries blooming in the grass and at the edge of the wood he found purple violets.

On up the river went the little skiff. The explorers came

to a spot where another stream flowed in among islands. "Three Rivers" they named this place, not realizing that one river could have so many channels. A few miles farther on, Champlain gave a cry of astonishment. A big lake lay just ahead — larger than any he had ever seen before. "Lake St. Peter," he called it, sure that he had reached the source of the St. Lawrence.

But the Indian interpreter guided Champlain's exploring party along the shores of Lake St. Peter for about thirty miles. Then the waterway narrowed once more. There were many islands — and now the adventurers were in the St. Lawrence again! Since leaving the Gaspé Peninsula, Champlain calculated that he must have journeyed nearly five hundred miles. Rivers in Europe were considered long if they were navigable for so much as fifty miles and with almost unbelieving joy, Sam began to picture the New World as it really was.

At the head of Lake St. Peter, the Indians with Champlain began to look anxiously over their shoulders and beg that the white chiefs would hurry on.

"What is the matter?" demanded Champlain, who needed time for his map making.

"The River of the Iroquois — it is there," they said. "Hurry! A war party may be coming down the river to rob us of the trade goods you have given us for our furs."

Champlain looked where the Indians pointed, but saw nothing except a rough barricade of upright logs. A few canoes were beached near by. Through an interpreter, an Ottawa warrior explained that his people had built the fence to keep the Iroquois at home. Champlain shook his head at the pitifully frail barrier. He hoped that someday he might have men enough to protect the Indians of the St. Lawrence region, so they could bring their furs down the river unmolested.

For some time now, Sam had been hearing the dull roar of rapids. Soon the sound was so loud that it made conversation impossible. Flecks of foam floated downstream, and the skiff no longer made any headway, although a good breeze filled her sail. The five members of the crew tried rowing — but it was no use. The current was too strong.

Champlain and Pontgravé clambered ashore, telling their men to tie up the boat, since she could go no farther. Some Indians who were with them paddled serenely on, but before long the rapids were too swift even for them. They lifted their canoes out of the water and carried them along a fairly well-marked path.

Sam found the going pretty hard. He was loaded down with his heavy flintlock musket, his steel helmet and his leather coat mounted with steel plates. "I feel like a clumsy ox," he muttered, as he floundered along, slapping at myriads of mosquitoes that swarmed about his head. How he envied the easy grace of the savages, striding far ahead up the rocky trail! The roar of water grew louder and louder. And now the trail turned, coming out on a rock above the river. Sam stopped, awestruck by the sight of what we now call the Lachine Rapids. A great mass of tumbling white water boiled among rocks, swirled past islands and thundered till no other voice could be heard. It's — it's unbelievable, thought Sam. He grew dizzy watching the river speed by.

The travelers labored along the bank for three miles. They could never hope to carry their heavy wooden boat overland, and Pontgravé was for turning back.

"Let us leave our heavy gear behind and travel in Indian canoes as soon as we pass the rapids," Champlain suggested.

But Pontgravé flatly refused to have anything to do with a canoe. "Why kill ourselves just to see more of this appalling wilderness?" he groaned. "Whoever heard of such a long river, anyway? People will not believe your map as it is."

To Champlain, the wilderness was beautiful, and each day brought new joy of discovery. He always felt that the best lay just around the corner. The season for crossing the Atlantic was short, however, and he knew they must leave before ice blocked the mouth of the St. Lawrence. With a heavy heart, he gave the order to turn back.

9 · *ABOARD THE SHIP* GOOD NAME

SAD NEWS awaited Champlain upon his return to France. His good friend the Sieur Commander de Chastes was dead. "This was a great affliction to me," said Sam as he thought how much he would miss the old soldier, who had been like a father to him.

Champlain no longer needed a sponsor at court, however. As soon as he arrived in Paris, the king sent for him, eager to see the work of the Royal Geographer. This time, Champlain carried a huge parchment map, and many a courtier cooled his heels in the antechamber while Henry IV studied the course of the St. Lawrence River. "Splendid!" cried His Majesty. "I could find it in my heart to envy you the chance to explore this wonderful country."

Remembering Henry of Navarre in the saddle during his fight for the throne, Sam knew the king spoke the truth. Champlain left the royal audience commissioned to go with the next expedition to New France. This was all the reward he sought.

Sam put his notes and his journal together to make a story of his voyage — then he went around to see a printer. *About Savages* was the name of the book which soon appeared. Almost overnight, *About Savages* became the talk of Paris, and Champlain was the author of a best-seller.

Since the fur monopoly had belonged to the Sieur de Chastes alone, the king had a right to grant it to someone else, now that De Chastes was dead. Henry let it be known that the exclusive right to trade with the Indians in New France would go to the highest bidder. Under De Chastes, the fur company had cleared fifty per cent profit on their investment, so plenty of people were interested.

At the king's court was a nobleman who came from the same part of France as Champlain, himself. This was Pierre du Gaust, Count de Monts, a Protestant who had helped Henry become king. He was now Gentleman in Ordinary of the King's Chamber and governor of the city of Pons. When he asked for a grant of land, the king gave him all of New France from the fortieth to the forty-sixth parallels of longitude. This private estate began somewhere around Philadelphia and ended beyond Montreal! It was called Acadia.

Three years later, King James of England granted most

of this same territory to the Virginia Company. Kings were forever giving away property that did not belong to them.

The Count de Monts was such a wealthy man that he could afford to buy the Canadian fur monopoly. An awful howl went up from Pontgravé, who wanted to buy the monopoly himself, and from seaport towns like Dieppe and La Rochelle, whose merchants saw themselves shut out of rich trade.

De Monts settled matters with Pontgravé by letting him buy a large interest in the new fur-trading company. A few merchants were satisfied the same way — the rest left to air their grievances at court. "Much good may it do them!" laughed de Monts, certain of the king's favor.

"You are now Viceroy of Canada," said Henry IV, as the papers were signed and sealed. "Remember, De Monts, my Royal Geographer goes with you to map your new land."

"With all my heart," agreed de Monts. "He shall help me establish my colony. De Champlain is the one man in all France who has seen the Spanish colonies which have succeeded so well."

When Champlain was consulted, he said that the St. Lawrence River would be the best place to start a town. But De Monts wanted to go farther south, where the winters would not be so cold. It was agreed that only men should go on the first expedition. "We will have houses built before any women and children come to New France," De Monts decided. He ordered beams and boards cut to measure and loaded on a vessel, so that his own house could be set up very quickly, once the site of the new colony was chosen. The idea of prefabricated homes is not so new, after all.

French people had made two previous attempts to colonize New France, and both times they had failed. Champlain tried to think why — so that past mistakes could be avoided. In 1535, Jacques Cartier built a sturdy little fort on the St. Lawrence above Quebec. He was prepared against human enemies, but hunger and disease conquered and the colony was abandoned. "I will take ample provisions," promised De Monts. "We must see if some good doctor will join our expedition."

The second French colony had been started by Captain Ribaut — a Huguenot. In 1562 he settled near the present city of Savannah, Georgia. Here there was a warm climate and enough food, but the settlement was too close to Spanish territory. With ruthless efficiency the Spaniards wiped out their French neighbors. "Thank God Acadia is a long way from New Spain," said Champlain. "But we must build a good fort and keep a sharp watch."

"I will hire some Swiss soldiers," said De Monts. "They will make the best possible guard for our colony."

Now handbills appeared all over Paris. Carpenters, bricklayers, blacksmiths, bakers — all were wanted to go aboard the ship *Good Name*. "TRY YOUR FORTUNE IN NEW FRANCE — HIGH WAGES, WONDERFUL OPPORTUNITY TO SEE THE NEW WORLD — so read the advertisements. There was terrible poverty at that time in France, but only about one hundred and twenty workmen were found who dared cross the sea.

De Monts hired two ships. The *Good Name* was the biggest, and he was proud of her. We think of the *Mayflower* as a very tiny vessel — but *La Bonne Renommé* was smaller still. Her name came from the French proverb "A good name is worth more than a belt of gold."

Champlain was disappointed that so few people cared to risk their lives crossing the ocean. Then one day he dropped into an apothecary's shop to buy some drugs to take on the expedition. "I have read your book, *About Savages*," said Louis Hébert, owner of the shop. "Do you think I could get a place on your ship? Here in Paris, it is all I can do to earn bread for my poor wife and children. I want land of my own, for I have a way with growing things. I want a home for my family, and I wouldn't mind building it myself."

"You're just the man for us," cried Champlain. "Hired workmen are all very well, but if our colony is to succeed we must have men who want a home, as you do. Besides, your knowledge of herbs will be most helpful to us."

"Oh, I have read great parchment books telling what plants to cut in the dark of the moon, and how to brew the leaves to cure many a strange disease," boasted Hébert. "Also, I can bleed a man as well as any barber."

"I doubt if our surgeon can do any more than that," smiled Champlain. And so Louis Hébert joined the expedition, to become one of the first genuine colonists of New France.

Very different, but just as welcome, was another recruit, the Baron de Poutrincourt. "I am sick of court intrigue," he said. "If New France is half as fine as you have painted it in your book, De Champlain, I am going to take my family and settle there. I will join the expedition first, and see for myself."

Not all the adventurers were grown men. One day the King's secretary, the Sieur de Boullé, spoke to Champlain. "I'm thinking of sending my son Eustace on your expedition," he said. "The boy loves adventure, and I think the experience would be the making of him. But his mother says he is too young. Come to my house, De Champlain — see if you can reassure my wife about the dangers of the voyage."

Champlain soon became a frequent visitor at the handsome town house belonging to the king's secretary. He took a great liking to Eustace. "I will treat him as a younger brother," Sam promised Madame Boullé. "I wish I had a brother like him." Eustace was given guns, a sword and servants of his own. He set out for New France as a gentleman adventurer — aged fourteen!

So little by little, fine people were drawn to the expedition. But others joined only for excitement, or to escape from some trouble they had gotten into at home. They all gathered at Dieppe, where De Monts's two vessels lay at anchor.

Now it was discovered that still more men were needed. "Take this order from the king," said De Monts to his sea captains. "Go through the jail and get as many men as you need."

Champlain was already aboard ship when he heard the tramping of feet. "Here come the jailbirds," shouted the captain. "I'm bringing you a fellow for your chart making." Sam looked up from a column of figures as the cabin door opened and a tall, broad-shouldered man was shoved inside. "This is Jean Something-or-other — not his real name, of course," Captain Morel said hastily. "He claims he's sailed to the Spanish Main — which I doubt."

The cabin was rather dark, but Sam liked what he could see of the new man. For a fellow just out of jail, he held his head surprisingly high. "Do you want to go on this voyage?" Sam asked. "Or are you signing on just to get out from behind bars?"

"I was given no choice," said the sailor, "but there is nothing in the world I would rather do than sail for New France with you, sir."

There was such a ring of gladness — almost laughter — in the man's voice, that Champlain was startled. I wish I could see him better, he thought. The fellow acts as though he knew me. Reaching in his pocket, he pulled out a handful of coins. "Here," he said, "go ashore and get yourself a decent outfit. But be quick, for we sail at the turn of the tide."

The new recruit thanked the Sieur de Champlain, then darted across the deck and hurried ashore.

Captain Morel groaned. "Whatever possessed you to turn him loose! There goes the only man who might know one rope from another, and now we'll never see hide nor hair of him again. The other felons are below decks, bound hand and foot till we are well out to sea."

Champlain smiled. "If my man comes back, I'll know what sort of fellow I've got. If not — I'd rather he'd play me false here than in the wilderness of New France."

In the excitement of putting to sea, however, Sam forgot his new man. The little ship was pitching in the choppy English Channel when a voice spoke out of the gathering darkness. "Here I am, sir. Have you any orders?"

Sam turned to look into a pair of singularly honest eyes. A seaman in a neat blue jersey and warm woolen breeches was standing at attention. His thick brown hair was neatly combed and his face, though pale, was freshly shaved.

"I would hardly know you," exclaimed Champlain, surveying the sailor with evident approval. "Were you able to buy everything you need? Have you a good knife, for example?"

White teeth flashed into a wide smile. "My own knife, I bought back first of all. Luck was with me, for the pawnbroker had not sold it. Please to look at it, sir."

"I see you prize this knife greatly," said Champlain, somewhat amused. He took the heavy double-edged dagger the seaman offered him.

"The best friend I ever had gave it to me when I was a boy," the seaman announced solemnly.

Sam studied the knife in the uncertain twilight. TOLEDO, it said on the blade, in little letters among a tracery of leaves. As though it were yesterday, Champlain remembered the day he bought that very dagger in St. Malo. He looked up at the seaman, and their eyes met.

"Daniel Haye," cried Champlain, grasping the seaman's hand.

For a moment, neither of them could speak. "Tell me what happened," said Sam at last.

"I was in jail for debt," Dan explained. "You see, I signed on a ship that paid extra well, so I gave my advance wages to my mother and borrowed more on my prospects of a prosperous voyage. I thought I would be home again in two or three years, with pockets bulging with Spanish gold."

"You weren't by any chance aboard the *Stella*, off Haiti?" suggested Champlain.

Dan gasped. "How did you know? We wrecked our ship to keep it from the filthy Spaniards. They chased us ashore, but the natives hid us. I was three years on the island of Haiti before a French ship picked me up."

"I was with the 'filthy Spaniards,'" laughed Sam. "I saw your mother and she told me of your voyage. The only thing I could do to help you was to stay away from there."

"You saw my mother?" questioned Dan eagerly.

"It was some time ago," confessed Sam, for he had been either in Paris or in New France ever since his return from Spain.

"I worked my passage home," Dan said, "but I was penniless when I landed in Dieppe. I pawned my knife to get money to go to St. Malo. Then my creditors caught me and I was clapped in jail. My poor mother! She will have to beg her bread in the street."

"Now don't give up hope," cried Champlain. "We're sure to drop anchor at St. Malo. I'll see that you get ashore — with all the advance pay you care to ask for."

"But — but those of us who were taken from jail get no pay at all," stammered Dan.

Just then Eustace Boullé came dashing along the deck, laughing with delight at his first taste of salt air. "A fine night, Sieur de Champlain," he called. "That your new man? You've picked a good one."

Off he went without pausing for a reply. The astonished look on Dan's face made Champlain laugh. "You see, I'm the King's Geographer — that's why the title. Now about your mother — the Sieur de Monts does not pay the men the king gives him from the jail — that is true. But he must supply me with someone for my mapping, and I always pay my people. You will have money to give your mother in St. Malo."

"I always wanted to be your man," Dan said.

Champlain nodded. "We planned it long ago," he agreed.

For a while the two men stood silent, listening to the slap-slap of waves against the ship. They were remembering the days when they were boys together. But almost at once their thoughts turned to the adventures that lay ahead. "I'll teach you to take soundings and help with my map," Champlain promised. "Oh Dan — wait till you see New France. It's bigger and more exciting than we ever imagined!"

10 · SUMMER IN THE WILDERNESS

Two LITTLE ships set out from Dieppe in April, 1604. Only one arrived at a small bay in Nova Scotia, a month later. This was the *Good Name*, with De Monts, leader of the expedition aboard, along with Champlain, Eustace and Dan. At first no one worried very much about the other vessel.

De Monts was in high good humor, because he found a trader with a ship full of furs in the very bay the *Good Name* chanced upon. Armed with a parchment signed by the king, he boarded the trader. "Your ship and all her cargo are hereby confiscated," he told poor Captain Rossignol. In all probability, this trader had no idea that De Monts had bought the fur monopoly. It made no difference — he lost everything. De Monts named the harbor

"Rossignol Bay," which must have seemed like an insult rather than an honor to the unfortunate trader he had just ruined.

Still the second vessel did not come, and De Monts got tired of waiting in Rossignol Bay — now called Liverpool. He began to cruise southward looking for a better harbor, and soon he saw one exactly to his liking. Everyone was tired of living on shipboard, so the *Good Name* anchored and the crew flocked ashore to build huts for themselves out of small trees and sod. Aboard the *Good Name* were two sheep in a pen. "Let's put them ashore, too, and give them a chance to graze," said the men. But it was no easy matter getting a sheep into a rowboat! One fell into the water and was drowned.

Now everybody began calling the place "Sheep Bay," or — as Champlain wrote in French on his map — "Mouton Bay." The place is called Mouton Bay to this day — though few people know why.

It was June now. Day after day, the sun shone, the sky was a flawless blue and the deep water of the bay sparkled joyously. The men from the *Good Name* were like boys on a camping trip. They shot wild duck and passenger pigeons. The trout fishing was splendid, and they never thought that summer would someday be over, and that good times must end.

The leaders of the expedition were beginning to be anxious, however. "Time is flying, while we wait for the provision ship," said Champlain. "Let me take a few men and explore southward."

"My pilot, Champdoré, can go," agreed De Monts.

"You can keep Champdoré," said Sam bluntly. "He is a stubborn, ignorant fellow, who knows nothing beyond the use of the compass. I cannot teach him the first thing about navigation. Just let me have my man Haye and a seaman or two."

But when Champlain asked for Dan, the Sieur de Monts objected. "I have made a serious mistake," De Monts confessed. "All our winter provisions are aboard my other vessel instead of being equally divided. Sooner or later, the men will realize that the bulk of our supplies are lost. Then there will be trouble, and I shall need your Daniel Haye — and every other loyal man."

"Give me the apothecary Hébert," suggested Champlain. "He's loyal, indeed, but not much of a fighter."

Hardly had Champlain left Port Mouton than he came upon a harbor so pretty he wrote *Port Joli* on his map, and so it stands today. Right close by was another, larger harbor. And now the Paris shopkeeper swelled with pride when he saw what his good friend Samuel de Champlain wrote upon his chart. More than three hundred years have passed, but the map of Nova Scotia still carries the name *Port Hébert!*

Two more weeks went by, and back at Port Mouton the provision ship still failed to appear. Dan awoke one night to hear two of his shipmates whispering together outside his hut. "Go on — tell him. He'll come in with us," said one man.

"He will not," said the other. "Take my advice and tie him up. Hurry! It's nearly dawn."

Dan felt for his trusty knife — then he came out of his

hut. "Hello, fellows," he said. "What's afoot?" By their voices he recognized two of his former jail-mates.

"Listen," said one, hastily. "We've just found out something. There's no more flour, no salt beef aboard ship. We've been tricked. All the winter's food was in the other vessel, and she sank weeks ago — or pirates took her. Come on. We're going to steal the *Good Name* and sail for home."

"What about the Sieur de Champlain? Would you leave him to die of starvation?" began Dan.

"Who cares? We're leaving all their lordships — they've tricked us, I tell you. Better a few should die than all. Come along before it grows light."

"Nothing doing," snapped Dan. Then he whirled around as the other man tried to jump him from behind. The fellow had a knife, but even in the darkness Dan managed to grab his wrist. They went down together with a crash, and rolled over and over on the ground. Now Dan had his own knife at his assailant's throat.

Dim forms came swarming from the circle of huts. Dan began to shout lustily for help as four men piled on top of him. They all had their knives out, but luckily they dared not use them for fear of killing each other in the dark. In the confusion, Dan twisted himself free.

De Monts leaped from his bed, calling to the Swiss guards. The Baron de Poutrincourt had the presence of mind to light a pine torch, and in the smoky glare the rebellious seamen saw the soldiers come running, muskets ready. This was more than any of them cared to face, and order was quickly restored.

The ringleaders were put in irons aboard the *Good Name*, but De Monts was obliged to reassure the rest of his people. "If our provision ship does not come soon, we will return to France," he promised sadly. "Be certain, however, that we will not abandon the Sieur de Champlain, nor anyone else!"

Three days later, an Indian was seen paddling rapidly into Mouton Bay. His haste suggested that he brought news, and sure enough, he carried a letter from Champlain. The missing provision ship had been found, all safe and sound! She was anchored in a hitherto unknown harbor fifty miles to southward, and Pontgravé, who was in charge, seemed not at all concerned about finding his leader. Providence, in the form of Samuel de Champlain, got the two ships of the expedition together again.

With Champlain to guide him, Pontgravé sailed to Mouton Bay. There he unloaded all his supplies into the trading vessel his leader had confiscated, and took the furs aboard. "Now let us hope the St. Lawrence Indians have brought mink and silver fox to Tadoussac," said Pontgravé, as he turned northward.

To the south sailed De Monts — more interested in finding a suitable spot for his colony than in trading with the Indians. They rounded a cape where sandy shoals almost grounded the *Good Name*. "Cape Sable," Champlain called it, because sable means sand in French.

At Cape Sable, the *Good Name* turned northward and traveled about eighty miles to the Bay of Fundy. Here they found a fine sheltered harbor which they called St. Mary's. Once more, everyone landed to pick berries and hunt rabbits, as though this were a summer vacation. A young priest from Paris named Nicholas Aubrey set out for a stroll with a few companions.

They came to a spring, and for the first time these city people saw clear, icy water bubbling up among moss-covered rocks. What a beautiful, peaceful spot it was! The young men sat down, and Nicholas took off the sword he was wearing, because it got in his way. As they lay about under the trees, someone unfortunately mentioned religion, and now the place was peaceful no longer, for a fierce argument broke out.

On the way back to the ship, Nicholas Aubrey and a Huguenot dropped somewhat behind the others, still disputing about their differing ideas. Then the priest noticed that he had left his sword back at the spring. Telling the Huguenot not to wait, he turned back.

But Nicholas Aubrey forgot that he was in a wilderness, not a park. Where could the spring be? He took a new direction — then turned again. Night fell, and the young man was lost.

Meanwhile, Champlain was sailing a skiff along the unexplored west coast of Nova Scotia. Twenty-five or so miles beyond St. Mary's Bay, they came to the mouth of a river. "This place is worth investigating," Champlain pointed out. "Notice what a great volume of water rushes between these headlands."

De Monts was doubtful, but they waited for an inflowing tide, and then Champlain took the tiller. The wind filled the sails of the little skiff, and for a few minutes they sailed smoothly into the unknown river. Then the boiling current snatched at them and whirled their boat as if it had been a chip of wood. "Look out!" yelled Champlain. And Dan, who was up in the bow with a boat-hook, fended them off a rock just in time. Now the southern headland loomed perilously close. Champlain heaved on the tiller — and they swept safely by.

A few breathless moments more and the sailing skiff shot clear of the narrows. The explorers gave a shout. They were not in a river at all, but in a beautiful, almost land-locked harbor. Waterfalls sparkled among the trees on shore, and in a broad grassy valley a herd of moose were feeding. Birds sang, and the air was sweet with the scent of balsam. "You should give your name to this place," the Sieur de Monts told Sam. "You were the one who urged us to enter."

This was the first important discovery of the voyage, and Sam's blue eyes were bright with joy. But he shook his head over De Monts's suggestion for a name. "I call this Port Royal," he said. "His Majesty's whole fleet could anchor here in safety and no lesser name will do."

The Baron de Poutrincourt was the most enthusiastic of all, as the adventurers sailed across Port Royal. "It is an earthly paradise," he cried. "Here I could pass all my days."

"It is yours, then," said De Monts carelessly. "I promised you a grant of land, you know."

"Why shouldn't we all settle here?" proposed Poutrincourt, who had no desire to keep the best for himself. Champlain agreed but De Monts had just been given half a continent and he was not going to settle in the first likely spot he saw. On they sailed along the Bay of Fundy, which bites deep into the land for a hundred and fifty miles.

The explorers made the full circuit of the Bay of Fundy and reached a point about opposite Port Royal. Here they found a harbor which the Indians called "Passamaquoddy." Champlain talked with Panonias, the Indian interpreter. "What does 'Passamaquoddy' mean?" he asked.

"Place of Pollock," replied the Indian. "We come here to fish. To live — no. This place not good."

But the Sieur de Monts was strangely attracted by Passamaquoddy Bay and the rivers that flow into it. "Look," he cried, "the streams seem to form a cross and that is surely a good omen. Let us name the largest river the 'St. Croix'" (which means Holy Cross). "And there is a beautiful little island covered with cedar trees and with sparkling white sandy beaches. Let us call it 'St. Croix Island.' We have found the ideal place for our new home!"

Champlain was much less enthusiastic. "Having found no place more suitable," he said, "we began to erect a barricade on a small islet a little removed from St. Croix Island, and this served as a platform for mounting our cannon. Each man worked so efficiently that in a very short time the island was put in a state of defense, although the mosquitoes, which are a sort of little fly, gave us great annoyance. Several of our men had their faces so swollen with bites that they could hardly see. The barricade being finished, the Sieur de Monts sent his longboat to tell the people who were on board our vessel in St. Mary's Bay to come to St. Croix."

A few days later, the *Good Name* arrived. The King's Geologist, who had gone in the longboat, came back with a curious tale. "I went to have another look for mineral deposits in St. Mary's Bay," he said. "I was poking about among the rocks on the shore when a queer black object caught my eye. 'That looks for all the world like a priest's hat,' I said to a couple of young sailors I had with me."

To the geologist's surprise, the sailors turned pale with fright. "You have been with the Sieur de Champlain," they stammered. "You have not heard the news. One day a young priest disappeared and we searched but never found him. We feel sure that poor Father Aubrey was murdered by a certain wicked Huguenot. And now — now he has come to haunt us because the crime was unpunished."

"I told the boys not to be so foolish," recounted the geologist. "I ran to the spot where I had seen the hat and there, on the ground, lay the young priest, more dead than alive. He was like a skeleton for he had lived on nothing but partridgeberries for sixteen days. But he smiled faintly when we picked him up and carried him safely to the ship."

It was a miracle, thought Champlain, that the young priest had been found just as the *Good Name* was about to sail away. Now perhaps there would be fewer bitter arguments between Catholics and Protestants at the settlement. He turned happily to the work he liked best — map making.

Champlain was now at work on a map of Passamaquoddy Bay and the island the settlers had chosen. This was the finest, most accurate he had ever drawn. Allowing for the fact that he used magnetic north instead of our "true north," it is wonderfully like the maps of today and it was used to settle the boundary between the Province of New Brunswick, Canada, and the State of Maine. The line between the United States and Canada now runs through St. Croix Island. On most modern maps, this island is now called "Dochet" — pronounced "dō shay" — and it bears a monument telling of the French settlers who lived there in 1604.

11 · WINTER COMES

WHAT shouts, what hustle and bustle broke the peace of the wilderness as the cargo from the *Good Name* was unloaded at St. Croix Island! For the first time in history, that particular part of America heard the ring of European axes as the little cedar trees toppled, one by one. Samuel de Champlain was completely absorbed in the kind of work he could do best. Proudly he wrote, "The Sieur de Monts proceeded to set workmen to building houses for our residence and allowed me to draw plans for the settlement.

"After the Sieur de Monts had chosen a site for the storehouse, which was 54 feet long, 18 feet broad and 12 feet high, he selected the plan for his own house. Then he assigned places to workmen and colonists, and they began to collect in fives and sixes according to their preferences. All set to work to clear the island, to fetch wood, to cut timber, to carry earth, and other things necessary to the construction of buildings.

"The work went forward steadily and vigorously: the carpenters at the storehouse and the dwelling of the Sieur de Monts, and all the others, each at his own. I worked at my house, which I built myself with the aid of some servants. This was forthwith finished and in it the Sieur de Monts lodged till his own house was ready."

On the last day of August, 1604, the settlers gathered on the shore of St. Croix Island to watch the *Good Name* sail away. Poutrincourt was going home to France to tell of golden summer days spent in his "earthly paradise." "I'll be back in the spring," he promised. "I'll bring fresh provisions and more settlers for this lovely land of New France."

Seventy-four men watched the white sails fade in the distance. Now De Monts and his handful of French colonists were the only white men on the North American Continent above the Spanish settlements!

Champlain set out at once with De Monts, to explore southward in their vessel. What a problem in map making the deeply indented coast of Maine was! Patiently, Sam charted each island and inlet and to this day a considerable sprinkling of French names mark his route. "Grand Manan" and "Petit Manan" were named by Champlain and in his journal he carefully described "Mt. Desert." "I went near an island about four or five leagues long," he said. "It is very high with notches here and there, so it appears, when one is at sea, like seven or eight mountains rising together. The tops of most of them are without trees because they are nothing but rocks. I called it, 'Isle des Monts Déserts.' "

The explorers sailed up the Penobscot River as far as the present site of Bangor, Maine, where they found an Indian town. Sam liked these Indians, some of whom he had seen trading at faraway Tadoussac. He asked them how they made that journey and they told of lakes and rivers which carried their canoes northward, mile upon mile. "This would be a good place for us to settle," counseled Champlain. "These Indians are friendly and intelligent. We could teach them to help us build a powerful colony like one of those in New Spain."

But the Sieur de Monts feared and distrusted all Indians and considered them good for nothing except to bring in furs. "It's a fine thing there are so few savages around St. Croix," was his opinion.

As the explorers left Penobscot Bay a storm arose. They had planned to continue southward but the winds threatened to dismast their vessel and the heavy seas almost swamped her every time they left the lee of the land. On the twenty-third of September, they put back toward the Bay of Fundy and, with head winds all the way, they were lucky to make St. Croix safely by October second.

A few sunny Indian summer days convinced the settlers that the rainy season was over. After all, they were in the same latitude as Spain, and well south of Champlain's native Southern France. He went blithely to work to plant a garden on the mainland which he described as "fairly big."

"I sowed a quantity of seeds," he said, "as did others who had any." On October sixth the snow began to fall!

Champlain went serenely to bed in the little cabin he had built for himself. After all, snow flurries, though not common, were sometimes seen back home in Brouage. When he awoke, it was morning, but his one small room was still dark. He raked aside the ashes and blew the coals to life upon the hearth. Looking out the window, he saw that snowflakes were still hurrying by.

Sam began to draw his map of the Penobscot River from rough sketches he had brought back from his trip. Time flew by while he was at this task he loved so well. At noon he saw to his amazement that the storm roared on, and he decided not to go to the house of the Sieur de Monts, where he and the other leaders always ate. Instead, he cooked himself some Indian corn in a big iron kettle over the fire. Friends had laughed at him for buying the corn from the Penobscots, and getting their squaws to show him how it was prepared. Well — they could laugh, he thought. The stuff was surprisingly good.

Toward night, the cabin grew chill and Champlain threw the rest of his wood on the fire. I'll have to get more from my woodpile outside, he said to himself. Then came an unpleasant discovery — his cabin door wouldn't open. Peering out the window, he saw that a three-foot drift was holding it shut. The room grew steadily colder, but by the time Sam had forced open his door, inch by inch, and shoveled a path to his woodpile, he was warm with exertion. The stack of wood looked alarmingly small under the snow.

Next morning, the sun shone on a dazzling white island. Here and there the roof of a cabin or the top of a chimney showed above the snow, like a child's head peering out from under a mound of bed-clothes. Champlain was out early, and the clear air tasted so good, he began to sing at the top of his lungs, as he cleared his front path.

A hail from across the way made him turn, and there was young Eustace Boullé, who shared a neighboring cabin with one of the priests. Eustace was knee deep in snow, and thrashing around like a playful puppy. Sam ducked, as a snowball whizzed past his ear!

Before long Dan joined Champlain and Eustace, and the Swiss soldiers turned out to help them shovel paths all over the settlement. "This reminds me of my Alpine village," said one of the Swiss, snuffling up great lungfuls of pine-scented air.

The first snow soon melted, but Champlain noted in his journal that whenever clouds gathered, snow fell, instead of rain. Three or four feet was the average depth all winter. By the third of December, cakes of ice began to float past the island from the north, and this was the most ominous sign of all. The firewood on the island was soon exhausted, and now ice in the river made trips to the mainland dangerous indeed.

If a boat could be launched, Dan could do it. As often as possible he rowed Champlain, Eustace and a Swiss soldier or two across the perilous river to cut wood. They took their guns along, and although they did not always have luck, there was usually a rabbit or two for the pot when they returned.

One day Eustace wandered off in search of game before the others had finished their tedious wood chopping. A few minutes later they heard him shouting something about a big animal. Fearing lest the boy was about to attack a bear single-handed, Champlain and Dan snatched up their guns and ran to his aid. They found him bending over some strange tracks. "It looks as if a huge animal with web feet had been by," said Eustace.

Champlain and Dan laughed, but when they looked at the tracks, they could think of no better explanation themselves. "Let's follow," proposed Sam. "An animal with feet like this would be worth seeing."

They floundered through the soft snow for over a mile, until they came to a place where deep hoofprints merged with the webbed tracks. "A moose was trying to run down this glade," said Sam. "Here he fell, but got up and struggled on."

"He's wounded," cried Eustace, pointing to fresh blood-stains on the snow.

The three friends followed cautiously until at last they saw a dark figure, crouching in a clump of hemlocks. "Ho, Sagamores," said an Indian, straightening up and raising his hand, palm outward.

"It's Panonias," exclaimed Champlain, recognizing one of the Penobscot interpreters.

But Eustace pointed excitedly. "Look — the savage has tennis racquets on his feet," cried the boy, staring at the first pair of snowshoes he had ever seen.

"Panonias go fast," said the Indian, proudly demonstrating. "Moose, he sink, and Panonias kill. White sagamores sink too — like moose."

Champlain laughed. "So this is our web-footed animal! I'll give you a good knife for a pair of web feet."

The Indian grunted. Maybe his squaw would see about making another pair of snowshoes. Meanwhile, he bargained shrewdly with the white men over some chunks of moose meat. "Game go away," he said, gesturing toward the snow-covered mountains. "Panonias go too. This place not good."

Next day all the settlers were invited to share the fresh moose meat, but the majority refused. "Just try some," urged Champlain. "It tastes like the finest beef from the roasting ovens on the Street of the Bears in Paris."

"Faugh!" said the Sieur de Beaumont, whose cabin was just south of Champlain's. "I have seen moose with their ugly faces and mammoth antlers. They look like nothing ever eaten by a Christian. Pass me the salt pork."

"You should come hunting with us. What have you been doing today?" Champlain asked.

The Sieur de Beaumont gave a short laugh. "I lay in my bed and wished I had never come to this Godforsaken country. I ordered my servants to cut wood, but the lazy fellows played at dice all day with your jailbirds. They say you went off to the mainland without them, De Champlain."

"They never presented themselves at the wharf," interposed the Sieur de Monts. "I advise you to see to your own men, and even cut wood yourself."

The young nobleman stared at his leader. "A pleasantry, I assume," he muttered. "I am not amused."

Sam's pride in the house he had built with his own hands began to evaporate. The cabin was made of green wood which now shrank, and great cracks opened up through which the wind howled dismally. "It was a poor shelter," he confessed, as he stuffed the chinks with sea-weed.

"During the winter a certain malady attacked our people," wrote Champlain, who was among the few to keep well. "It is called 'land sickness,' otherwise scurvy, according to our learned men."

"The forests bring us this illness," said the doctor at St. Croix. He was doubtless considered one of the "learned men," as he went about opening veins and drawing off blood, to cure his patients.

The writings of Samuel de Champlain show him to be far ahead of his time in many ways. His own ideas about scurvy were remarkably close to modern scientific knowledge, for he wrote: "To my mind, scurvy is brought on by eating salt meat and dried vegetables, with no fresh food of any kind." Today, scurvy is known as a vitamin-deficiency disease.

Before long the learned doctor of St. Croix was dead, and so were many of his patients. Louis Hébert, the Paris apothecary, took over. First, he had a talk with his friend Champlain. "You are one of the strongest men left in the settlement," he said. "Yet whenever it is possible, you hunt in the forest. If forest air is poison — why are you alive?"

"If forest air could kill — why don't the savages die?"

countered Champlain. "Yet they are stronger of arm, swifter of foot than we! To my mind, the food they eat and the outdoor life they live protect them from land sickness."

Hébert nodded approvingly. "You have prepared your queer Indian dishes for me, and I grow to like them. That strange little shellfish, the clam, is sweet and good — once you get used to it. Even the coarse yellow corn is good food, when carefully cooked. Our dainty Parisian friends insist on white flour from the storehouse, but if I can make them eat like the Indians — perhaps the priest will not be saying so many prayers for the dead!"

The apothecary made clam broth and corn soup, but many of his patients were too far gone. They had terrible sores in their mouths, and their teeth dropped out. Spring, with its fresh herbs and vegetables, came too late. Out of seventy-nine men, thirty-five died, and by April, twenty more were too weak to stand. "We had snow up to the end of April," wrote Champlain. He had counted on replanting his garden, but nothing could be done.

Provisions of all kinds were running low now, and what was left in the storehouse was frozen solid. "Let me cut you a pound of cider, Eustace," said Dan. Once the boy would have laughed, but now he was so hungry, he could hardly manage a smile.

"The provision ships will come soon," encouraged Champlain. "They must have left France already."

Week after week went by, however, and still no sail broke the terrible monotony of the broad bay. At last, De Monts called a conference. "Our friends are long overdue," he admitted, "and we have no ship save two long-boats. We must send a skiff northward, to search for a Grand Banks fisherman. We can pay him to take us back to France before we all die of starvation." De Monts's eyes clouded with grief as he surveyed the pitifully small group of men before him. "Gentlemen," he said, "our settlement has failed."

Silence fell, while several weary, half-starved adventurers nodded agreement. Then Samuel de Champlain rose to his feet. "Wait," he pleaded. "Our gardens have begun to grow, and already, game is more plentiful. Wait only six weeks more, and the ships will come. Why talk of failure, now that winter is past! I tell you, spring is here, and we are going to win!"

A few tired faces brightened, and there was a straightening of sagging shoulders. "Why not hang on a bit longer?" said one.

"The fishing fleet will be at Canso all summer," said another.

De Monts reached out and gripped Champlain's hand with gratitude. "It's agreed — eh gentlemen?" he cried. "We wait, and I believe the ships will come."

12 · SAIL ON THE HORIZON

As THE conference broke up, young Eustace Boullé sought out his friend, Champlain. "You saved the day," he cried. "Everyone was ready to quit till you spoke up."

"I didn't hear the Sieur de Boullé asking to go home to his mother." Champlain put his arm around the boy's thin shoulders. "Get your gun, Eustace. We'll have to feed these people, or they will lose heart all over again. Meet me at Dan's hut."

Since Daniel Haye was only a seaman, he had not been invited to the conference of titled gentlemen. Champlain told him the news. "Of course we can hold out a while longer," said Dan. "Look to southward — there's a flight of wild duck heading our way. Soon, the lakes will be black with them, and we shall have so much fresh game, we shall be as fat as a Paris pastry cook."

"We have a long way to go before we are fat," laughed Champlain. "Here comes Eustace. Tell me, now — which is boy, and which is gun? They're equally skinny!"

Eustace heard the remark, and grinned. "You should talk, you scarecrow," he countered. "What would your tailor say to the fit of that doublet?"

"Now as for me, I am used to going hungry," boasted Dan.

The three friends joked with one another cheerfully, but not one of them had the strength to row the boat very far without resting. Each pretended not to notice when the others paused for breath, or to let a spell of dizziness pass.

At last they found a little inlet on the St. Croix where wild duck were feeding. They pulled the boat under overhanging branches close to shore, and waited. Luckily, these ducks were not accustomed to hunters, and soon, a good many plump brown birds swam well within gunshot. The hungry men raised their fowling pieces and shot simultaneously. A great cloud of frightened birds rose from the river, as the echoes of the shooting rolled among the hills. But a respectable number of duck lay dead on the water. Champlain and Eustace gathered them in, while Dan rowed the boat.

It was almost dark and the hunters were heading back toward St. Croix Island when they saw an Indian squaw wandering about in a swamp. Every so often she would bend over, as though gathering something from the ground, although the white men saw nothing anyone could want. Always interested in Indian ways, Champlain paused to watch.

Here and there, silvery green fern shoots were just beginning to sprout. The squaw picked them and put them in a basket of woven rushes. Champlain made signs, as though eating, and she smiled and nodded. He climbed out of the boat and gathered some ferns for himself, but when he started to eat one raw, she shook her head. By means of wonderfully expressive sign language she explained that the "fiddle-heads" must first be boiled in a kettle.

The settlers greeted fresh roast duck with shouts of joy. By now they were too hungry to be prejudiced against strange foods and the fern-fronds were also well received. Properly cooked, they tasted somewhat like asparagus, and they were the first green vegetable seen on the Sieur de Monts's table in months.

Four weeks went by, and still the relief ships did not come. It was now the fifteenth of June. The gardens were doing well, game was plentiful, but those in charge of the settlement knew that help must come from France, if the colony were to go through another winter. Late at night the Sieur de Champlain paced back and forth on the log platform beside the little brass cannon. Bitterly, he questioned his own judgment. Just because he loved this land, was it right to encourage the others to hope and hang on?

The moon rose, laying a path of light like a pale golden carpet across the water. It must be about eleven o'clock,

Champlain thought. What a beautiful night it was, and how content he would be, if only all were well with the settlement! As the explorer stared sadly across Passamaquoddy Bay, he saw a narrow, black shape glide into view along the moon track! He rubbed his eyes and looked again, sure that anxiety and weariness were playing tricks with his mind. But there could be no mistake — a small boat was approaching.

Sam looked to the priming of the brass cannon. Savages! he thought. But is it a friendly visit — at this time of night? A moment more, and he would rouse the settlers. But now the wind shifted a trifle, and he caught the sound of oar-locks and voices. This was a ship's longboat, and her crew were certainly taking no pains to be quiet.

Champlain cupped his hands at his mouth and shouted in his deepest quarter-deck voice — "Ahoy there! Who comes?"

Faint and clear across the water the answer came — "Friends. We are friends from France!" Champlain stood silent for a moment, a prayer of thanksgiving in his heart. Then he leaped for the little cannon, drew the iron ball with which it was loaded, and fired salute after salute. All the surrounding hills gave back the rousing welcome.

Doors flew open and the settlers came tumbling out of their beds, sure that the Spaniards were upon them. "To arms!" shouted De Monts.

Then he saw Champlain running toward him, crying, "The ships have come! Our friends are here!" De Monts put up his sword and ran to raise the "Lilies of France" high on the flag-staff, on top of his house. By the time the longboat reached St. Croix Island, all the settlers who were strong enough to stand were waiting at the little dock, while trumpeters sounded a fanfare.

The Sieur de Pontgravé sprang ashore, followed by the Sieur de Poutrincourt. "Our ships are only six leagues down the coast," they said. "We left them at anchor when darkness fell, and hurried forward to bring you the good news. Thank God we find you safe!"

The Sieur de Poutrincourt looked around. Seventy-nine hale and hearty men had seen him off for France. Now the flaring pine torches lit up the gaunt faces of only eleven settlers. "At least I see some of you," said Poutrincourt, with a catch in his voice.

"There are twenty more unable to leave their beds," De Monts told him. "The food you bring will soon make them strong and well."

"And — and the rest?"

"God rest their souls," said De Monts. "And may I be forgiven for leading them to their death in the wilderness."

Although the ships were more than two months late, their arrival put fresh courage into the hearts of the settlers. "We must find a warmer, better-sheltered spot for our town," said De Monts. "There, we will build anew."

Within a week, he and Champlain were off exploring. Dan went along, and so did Eustace. Louis Hébert eagerly joined the party, hoping to discover new kinds of Indian food and fresh herbs.

They cruised along the coast of Maine, and as before, De Monts left all dealings with the Indians to Champlain. Sam had a knack for getting on with savages. He had

brought Panonias along as interpreter, and he went fear-lessly among strange tribes. Although they often began a war dance when they saw him, a judicious passing out of presents soon put a stop to that. Feasting followed, Champlain often supplying a deer or moose. Peace pipes appeared, and Sam smoked with old chiefs in dim lodges, and asked questions that pleased the savages, because they saw he really loved their land.

In the valley of the Saco River, Champlain for the first time saw Indians tilling the soil. With Hébert the apothecary at his heels, he walked among the women who hoed with crude instruments. Some had a clamshell fastened to a stick, while others dug with the bent root of a tree.

"Surely, this is a kind of lentil," said Hébert, eagerly examining the bean vines. And the Indian women tried to explain about a strange vegetable we call pumpkin and another, which was a kind of squash.

"This land is rich and good," Champlain told De Monts. "They have snow, but it does not last forever. Why not start our colony here, and soon we would live well, whether provision ships reach us from France or not."

But De Monts was interested chiefly in the fur trade. He pointed out that the Indians on the Saco had only a few foxskins which they wore in winter.

"We can teach these savages to trap furs for us, or bring them from the north, in order to get our trade goods," argued Champlain.

But De Monts thought no one could teach savages. On went the explorers, still looking for the ideal spot of the Sieur de Monts's dream. They passed the silvery beaches we call Old Orchard, Wells and Ogunquit, where present-day crowds love to gather in the summer time. In 1605, the long sands were empty, even of Indians.

After rounding Cape Ann, the explorers realized that they had seen their last birch-bark canoes! Now, the Indians came out to their ship in dug-outs made from hollowed logs. The interpreter, Panonias, could not understand a word these new savages said. He relapsed into a sullen silence, after making it clear that people who could not speak his language must be enemies.

Champlain had Daniel Haye row him ashore in what is now Salem Harbor. It was annoying to have to get along without an interpreter. He gave each of the Indians on shore a knife and a biscuit. They were almost as pleased with the strange new food as with the miraculous weapon. "I made them understand as best I could that they should show me how the coast trended," he said.

"They pictured for me another bay which they represented as very large. There they placed pebbles at equal intervals, giving me to understand that each represented a tribe and a chief." So Champlain wrote in his journal. Some hours' sailing brought the explorers into Massachusetts Bay, where they found a powerful Indian nation.

These savages possessed more cleared land than Champlain supposed existed in North America. Yet, their hatchets were of stone — "made of the stone we use in our guns," as Champlain put it, referring to the flint used in firing muskets. How could these Indians fell trees and clear land with stone axes?

Even without an interpreter, Sam managed to learn that

the trees were first girdled with fire, then left to die. A year later, the dead trees were pulled down and dragged away. Stumps were burned out, and the new field was ready to plow with stone or wooden implements.

Next day, the explorers sailed into Plymouth Harbor, where they found eight Indian houses built of bark, each with its garden in front. Along the shore, pits about five feet deep were dug, and corn was stored inside in woven grass sacks. It was then covered with sand, which rose in mounds about three feet above the ground.

Fifteen years later, in 1620, the Pilgrims sailed into Plymouth Harbor. The Indians were gone — which was a good thing, as they were far from friendly. But maize was still lying in the pits, just as Samuel de Champlain saw it. Noticing the series of low mounds by the shore, the Puritans opened them and discovered the hoard of corn, which saved the Plymouth Colony from death by starvation.

Leaving Plymouth, Champlain sailed south, thinking he was following the coast. Suddenly the keel of the little sailing vessel grated on sand. They pushed her off just before she stuck fast. Tacking, they sailed confidently on, when dead ahead they found shoal water once more. "Make for the open sea," ordered Champdoré, De Monts's pilot. Due east they went, but just as they all began to breathe more freely — there was the land again! Champdoré was terrified, and vowed he would never sail again where the land pursued a ship, no matter which way she turned!

Champlain only laughed, his face alight with joy. "White Cape," as he called Cape Cod, was evidently long and curved, reaching far out from shore. How interesting it looked on his map, even with only one side drawn in! Would the cape prove to be wide or narrow, indented or without harbors on the other side? Champlain could hardly wait to see, so he sent Dan out in the longboat to take soundings and find a passage around Cape Cod for the explorers' pinnace.

Much to the timid Champdoré's relief, they rounded Cape Cod safely and proceeded along the Atlantic shore. Now Champlain could draw in the rest of this curious peninsula, and he saw that it was like a bony finger, beckoning the unwary sailor toward treacherous shoals. There were no harbors for at least thirty miles, so the explorers were glad to put in at Nauset. They called it "Malbarre," or "Bad Bar," because a bar of sand at the entrance nearly wrecked the ship.

In spite of warnings, the crew had become careless in their dealings with the Indians. Five men went ashore with copper kettles for water — but they carried no guns. Searching among the sandy hills, they found a spring some distance from the shore. Savage eyes watched them, and coppery brown forms lay hidden in the underbrush.

A carpenter from St. Malo was the first to fill his kettle. He had put it aside to help the others, when an arm reached out from behind a bush and snatched it. "Leave that alone!" shouted the carpenter, but the Indian was already running off through the trees.

Some of the sailors started in pursuit, but instantly the woods were alive with savages, armed with bows and arrows, and with tomahawks. The St. Malo man was the first to see that he was running headlong into a deadly ambush. He whirled around — "Back, men!" he gasped. "Back to the ship!"

The Frenchmen turned and plunged through the underbrush in a frantic rush for the beach. "Help! Help!" they shouted. The hills mockingly echoed their cries, while out in the harbor, their vessel rocked serenely on the rising tide.

13 · THE FIGHT ON THE BEACH

THREE or four Indians wandered about the deck of the explorers' vessel. Wherever the ship anchored, savages were apt to come aboard out of curiosity. They stared at the mast and the reefed sails, puzzled over the compass, and touched the little brass cannon in the bow with respectful fingertips. Champlain kept a sharp eye on them, knowing that anything movable would disappear if he turned his back.

Suddenly, frantic shouts broke the silence of uninhabited Nauset Harbor. With one accord, the Indians aboard the pinnace made a break for the rail. "Hold them!" shouted Champlain, grabbing the savage nearest him. No one else moved quickly enough, and the other Indians dived cleanly over the rail and swam away.

As members of the crew tied up their only hostage, Champlain snatched a heavy arquebus and ran to the bow of the boat, shouting to Dan for a slow match. While waiting for Dan to strike a spark with flint and steel, in order to light the slow-burning fuse, Sam watched the drama on the beach.

The French sailors ran clumsily like men in a nightmare, for the soft sea sand dragged at their feet. At first, the savages stayed among the trees, but the minute their fellow tribesmen from the pinnace were in the water, they broke cover and sped lightly down the beach after their victims.

Now Dan handed Champlain the glowing fuse. He plunged it into the touchhole of his gun, and the heavy piece roared like the small cannon that it was. The recoil of the arquebus would have knocked down an ordinary man, but Champlain knew just how to brace himself and take the mighty blow on his steel-plated shoulder guard. The Sieur de Monts's arquebus roared a moment later, and Eustace fired his matchlock musket. The Indians fled to the cover of the woods.

Luckily, there was another rowboat aboard the pinnace. Champlain, Eustace, De Monts and Poutrincourt climbed aboard, carrying their lighted fuses and their clumsy weapons. Dan and other crew members rowed them toward shore as fast as possible. Holding their guns high in air, they jumped into the water the minute the boat's keel grated on the beach.

But the Indians had come out of the woods again. They sent a shower of arrows after the fleeing Frenchmen, and the carpenter fell face downward, a quivering shaft sticking from his back. The Indians were upon him instantly. Sam saw them plunge their knives into his helpless body.

Champlain sifted fresh powder into the touchhole of his arquebus. As he splashed ashore, he lowered the burning fuse, but close beside him someone stumbled, jostling his arm. There were a flash and a deafening roar. The arquebus had blown up right in his hands, and Champlain fell forward.

Dan and Eustace caught their friend and dragged him clear of the water, although they were almost blinded by the explosion themselves. "Take care of him, Dan," cried Eustace. "He would want me to carry on the fight." The boy dashed up the beach, priming his matchlock as he ran. His face was white with grief and anger. Let me get at those savages, he thought — for he felt sure his dearest friend was dead.

Without hope, Dan unfastened Champlain's helmet and loosened the heavy steel-plated jacket. He put his hand over Sam's heart, and then a smile of joy lit up his face. Champlain was not dead. He was only unconscious from the force of the explosion.

By this time, the Indians had melted away into the woods. With difficulty, De Monts kept Eustace from dashing after them into certain death by ambush. The boy walked sadly back toward the boat. Already, men were beginning to dig a grave, and he turned away his head. There would soon be two graves on this lonely shore, he thought.

Then a heavy hand clapped him on the shoulder and a

familiar voice said, "Well, young man, I see I missed the fight. That wretched arquebus almost killed me."

Eustace let out a half-hysterical shout as he looked into the powder-blackened face, minus eyebrows, and with the neat Vandyke beard now badly singed. "You — you scared me half out of my wits," he laughed. "Wait till you see yourself in a mirror."

Later that day, the leaders of the exploring party sat in conference over what to do with the Indian prisoner. Champlain had contrived to talk with him by means of signs, and a word or two of Micmac — the language of Nova Scotia Indians. "He expects to be killed because of the death of our carpenter," said Champlain. "I think also he expects some form of torture — although without words, it is hard to understand."

But the French explorers were civilized men, believing in the highest religious principles. They could not kill in cold blood, so they let the prisoner go. "Tell your people the white chiefs come in peace, not with the sword," said Champlain.

Not even the Indian interpreter, who had lived for months with the explorers, understood this generous act. The white men were cowards, the Indians thought. It took long years of patient teaching before they learned to respect men less cruel than themselves.

It was time now for the explorers to return to St. Croix. To their bitter disappointment they had not found the ideal spot for a new settlement. Certainly, the climate around Cape Cod was pleasant, but these Massachusetts Indians were hostile, and not to be trusted. "How about Port

Royal?" urged the Sieur de Poutrincourt. He was still as
much in love with the place as he had been the first time
Champlain led him through the narrow strait into the wide
bay.

This time, De Monts agreed to make Port Royal the
site of his colony.

The explorers hastened back to St. Croix where they
carefully took down the house De Monts had built, and
loaded it once more aboard ship. The storehouse was moved
across the Bay of Fundy, also, but the flimsy huts that
Champlain had once regarded with pride were not worth
salvaging. They were abandoned, and the wilderness took
over St. Croix Island once more.

In the absence of the explorers, another ship had arrived
from France. She brought welcome provisions, but disastrous news! The Sieur de Monts had been away from court
too long, and had trusted the king too much. Now rivals
were trying to ruin him by offering the king huge sums
of money for the fur monopoly. Although De Monts had
clearly understood that the monopoly was his for life, he
knew he must hurry to France to try to persuade the king
not to sell it over again.

Calling a council of leaders, De Monts explained the situation. "The Baron de Poutrincourt has promised to go to
France with me to use his influence with the king, and to
recruit new settlers for our colony," he said. "The Sieur
de Pontgravé agrees to remain here in New France to trade
with the Indians and to keep away rival fur traders, if he
can. Is there anyone else willing to face another winter here
in this wilderness?"

Champlain volunteered at once. "I would not think of going back to France till my map of this region is complete," he said. "During our first exploration we found evidences of mineral deposits, you know. Now I must see that the 'Bay of Mines' is thoroughly charted, before I present my map to the king."

A smile momentarily lighted the care-worn face of the Sieur de Monts. "And nothing would please His Majesty better than the prospect of gold and silver from Canada!" he agreed. The king's mining expert also promised to remain at Port Royal for further exploration.

Although Eustace Boullé had not seen his father and mother in over a year, he eagerly volunteered to stay at the settlement. Daniel Haye would not for the world leave his friend Champlain, and Louis Hébert, the Paris apothecary, promised to take care of the health of the colony for another year. In all, forty-five men agreed to live at Port Royal during the coming winter. They were really braver than the original seventy-five at St. Croix Island, because they knew what dangers and privations lay ahead.

Once more, Champlain was asked to help choose the site of the settlement and draw up the plans. He had learned from bitter experience that an easily defended island would not do. This time, he looked to the mainland, where no icy river could cut off the settlers from their source of firewood. The spot where the Annapolis River flows into Annapolis Basin seemed the logical place for a town. Time vindicated Champlain's choice, for later this became the site of Annapolis Royal, important British naval base. But De Monts overruled the geographer's judgment, and the first

French settlement was at a place now called Lower Granville, across Annapolis Basin.

The picture map of Port Royal which has come down to us today shows great improvement over the St. Croix venture. Separate cabins had proved wasteful of labor and material so, this time, Champlain designed long, narrow houses around an open square. Perhaps he got his idea from the Indian "long house," but he improved upon it greatly, for each settler had private quarters partitioned off, each had his own fireplace and chimney, and each, a front door to himself. These sturdy, contiguous houses provided walls easy to defend, while entrances to the inner court were well guarded with cannon. The Sieur de Champlain was becoming a fortress architect of excellent ability.

By the time the Sieur de Monts sailed to France, the new colony stood ready to face a wilderness winter. The days of safe sailing weather were numbered, but Champlain took a skiff and explored the west coast of Nova Scotia, carefully mapping each river and inlet. Small wonder that the task was a long one. Nova Scotia has a coastline more than three times as long as the entire Pacific shore of the United States.

Optimistically, Champlain named a promontory "Cap d'Or," or Cape of Gold, thinking he saw signs of wealth that would make Canada the equal of Spanish America. In this he was deceived but, basically, Champlain's dream was true for, many years later, Canada proved to have some of the world's richest gold mines.

When stormy winds finally drove Champlain back to the shelter of Port Royal Harbor, he found that twelve men in the settlement were already sick with the scurvy. So the sad story of the previous winter was to be repeated, thought Sam. But he remembered his own method of preventing this disease — fresh food and plenty of sunshine. Each morning he set out, axe on shoulder, to clear land for a garden. And every night when he returned to the settlement, he brought fresh fish to eat with wholesome Indian corn.

Champlain tells in his journal how he got his fish: "I surrounded my garden with ditches full of water, wherein I placed some very fine trout. Three brooks of clear running water flowed through my plot, from which the greater part of water for our settlement was supplied. I constructed, near the seashore, a little sluiceway, to draw off the water whenever I desired. This spot was completely surrounded by meadows, and there I arranged a summer house under beautiful trees, in order that I might enjoy the fresh air." All during his boyhood at Brouage, Sam had seen how the salt farmers brought in sea water by means of ditches, and how they held it with tide gates till the precious load of salt was deposited. No wonder it occurred to him to use the plentiful fresh water at Port Royal. Down by the shore, as he tells us, he "constructed a little reservoir to put salt fish, which we took when we needed them."

Dan and Eustace were always at Champlain's side, helping him with the delightful projects his lively imagination suggested. When work was done, they often strolled along the shore to an inlet where the sound of axes and saws could be heard. The pilot, Champdoré, was building a boat.

"Champdoré, my friend, as a shipwright you do very well indeed," Champlain would say, as he watched the little eight-ton vessel gradually take shape. "We shall have a fine voyage of discovery in this ship. Who knows what wonders we may behold from her decks, when spring comes again."

Beaming with pride, Champdoré indicated a rough scaffold of newly cut timber. "This pinnace is turning out so well that I am going to start another," he said. And so, in 1605, the shipbuilding industry was begun in Nova Scotia. As time went by, many a master yacht designer learned his trade in Nova Scotia shipyards, and many a "Bluenose" fishing schooner outsailed all her rivals in every race.

The winter passed rapidly for Champlain and his friends. These cheerful, busy people set a good example to the other colonists, who also tried to find useful work to do and, this time, scurvy did not spread. Five of those who were taken ill actually recovered, which was quite a triumph.

By March, the new pinnace was ready to put to sea, and Pontgravé decided to cruise southward in her, to trade for furs. Of course Champlain eagerly joined the party, hoping to make new discoveries to add to his map. They should have waited for more settled weather, as they soon learned through bitter experience.

14 · AT THE MERCY OF THE WAVES

THE FIRST NOVA SCOTIA-BUILT vessel set out on the 16th of March, 1606, with Champdoré as captain. If only he were as good a navigator as he is a shipbuilder, thought Champlain — for Sam was still struggling in vain to teach this stubborn man the use of navigation instruments. Champdoré crossed the Bay of Fundy, anxious to get into the lee of some harbor on the coast of Maine before nightfall.

A strong south wind was blowing, and after slogging into heavy seas all day, Champlain figured that they had covered only about eighteen leagues, or some forty-five miles. Land loomed dead ahead. "Is it the coast?" anxiously inquired Champdoré.

The geographer showed him the map. "We are off the island of Grand Manan," said Champlain. "We can sail safely on this course all night. Let us head straight for the Great White Cape, and waste no time following the coast — until we come to parts still unknown."

But Champdoré was terrified at the idea of setting a course into the open ocean. He insisted on anchoring for the night in a sandy cove, open to the sea and the south wind.

During the night the wind increased. Champlain paced the deck in a fever of anxiety, trying to see the dark loom of the land against the night sky. Surely the land was closer! They were dragging their anchor. "Hoist the lug-sail," shouted Champdoré, hoping to gain time to get up the anchor and escape from the cove after all. He spoke too late. The anchor rope parted! In Champlain's own words, they were "at the mercy of God and the waves."

A few moments more and the helpless pinnace was in the surf. She struck a rock, was held there, and everybody on board felt that the end had come. Soon the ship would crack up, and they began to calculate their chances of being able to make shore with perhaps the aid of a bit of wreckage.

Then came a breaker, higher than the rest. This is the end, Champlain said to himself, but the wave lifted the pinnace clear of the rock and deposited her high on the sandy beach. The explorer tells the story himself: "The bark being aground, we immediately began to unload what was in her to see what the damage was. It was not so great as we had imagined, and she was speedily repaired by the diligence of Champdoré, her master. When she was refitted, we reloaded her and awaited fine weather, and for the fury of the sea to abate. This did not happen for four days."

Not long ago a strange old anchor was brought up at Seal Cove on Grand Manan Island. Some say that this was the very one lost by Champlain's ship in 1606 — but others think that the anchor is still to be found, somewhere under the sea at White Head Island, southeast of Grand Manan.

This first voyage of the Nova Scotia-built pinnace was short, because Pontgravé was taken ill. Back they went to Port Royal, not to set out again until April. And almost at once poor Champdoré had trouble sailing the vessel he had built so well.

It was a rainy, foggy night. The explorers were still in that dangerous passage which separates Annapolis Basin from the Bay of Fundy. Champdoré anchored, but the next morning before daybreak he went below deck and awoke the Sieur de Pontgravé. Should he, or should he not, weigh anchor and get under way? The fog was still thick, and Champdoré could not make up his mind what to do.

"Oh, use your own judgment," said Pontgravé, annoyed at having his sleep broken.

Champlain also was awakened, and he told what happened next. "As Champdoré sought to pass through the entrance to the port, we were suddenly carried by the tide out of the passage, and were upon the rocks on the east-northeast side, before we had seen them. Pontgravé and I, who were in bed, heard the sailors crying out, 'We are lost.' This threw me to my feet to see what had happened.

"I was no sooner on deck than the bark was cast upon the coast and the wind, which was north, drove us on a point of land. We unfurled the mainsail, set and hoisted it as high as we could, in order to drive ourselves still farther upon the rocks.

"At the first bump of our boat upon the rocks, the rudder was broken, part of the keel and three or four planks stove in and some ribs smashed. All we could do was to wait until the tide ran out to get ashore. Otherwise, we risked our lives, because of the swell, which was very great and furious all around us.

"The tide having at length ebbed, we went ashore amid the storm, and immediately unloaded the pinnace of her contents. We saved a good part of the commodities in her, with the help of an Indian chief and his companions, who came to us in their canoes.

"The bark, being all battered, went to pieces on the return of the tide. We praised God for saving our lives from this shipwreck, from which we did not expect to escape so easily."

But the Sieur de Pontgravé was in no mood to praise his pilot, Champdoré. Anyone could see that the poor fellow was heartbroken over the loss of the little ship he had built and loved so well. But Pontgravé had him put in irons, and promised to take him to France to be tried in court for ruining the pinnace "with malicious intent."

In vain, Champlain pleaded the cause of the pilot, whom he described as "no-wise qualified to navigate," but "skilled in building vessels." Champdoré remained a prisoner for more than two months. "Why not take the handcuffs off him, so that he can at least finish that other pinnace," suggested Champlain. Finally Pontgravé agreed.

It was now the middle of June, and the provision ships which should have come from France toward the end of March had not been seen. The settlers were not suffering from starvation, because they had learned to live off their new land. Plenty of European goods were still needed, however, such as powder and shot, and even clothes and shoes. Pontgravé decided to take the new pinnace and sail north to the codfisheries at Canso, to ask for news.

Once more, the pilot Champdoré set out as captain of a ship he had built, and once more, ill luck dogged his heels. They got as far as the present town of Yarmouth, on the southern tip of Nova Scotia. Hardly one sixth of their journey was done when a squall came up and Champlain said that breakers ran "mountain high" along the coast. They dared not try to land, for it took two men at the tiller to keep the ship on her course. At the height of the storm there came a sharp crack, and the tiller swung loose. The iron braces holding the rudder had broken!

The little ship could only run before the wind. If a rock had loomed up before her, they would have been powerless to avoid it. Pontgravé could think of only one thing to do — he put his unfortunate pilot in irons again!

Dan proposed a "sea anchor," and Champlain helped him to lash together some boards to trail in the water behind the boat. This cumbersome float was supposed to hold back the ship but it cut their speed hardly at all. "We saw clearly that unless God aided us by other means, this one would not preserve us from shipwreck," said Champlain.

At this point, a message came from Champdoré. If the Sieur de Pontgravé would set him free, he thought he could mend the rudder! It didn't take Champlain long to make the angry Pontgravé listen to reason.

The pilot took some rope, cut it and very cleverly mended the rudder in the midst of that howling gale. "Surely you will withdraw your charges against this unfortunate man," begged Champlain. "Tell him you will not take him to France to face trial, after all!" Reluctantly, Pontgravé agreed.

The voyage in search of news from France was resumed, but it was not necessary to go all the way to Canso. A few miles farther on they met a sailing shallop coming their way! French sailors aboard her explained that the ship *Jonas*, with the Sieur de Monts in charge, was headed for Port Royal.

Champlain found the *Jonas* already at anchor when he returned. She was long overdue because of an accident which happened back in France. While she was being loaded at La Rochelle a squall had come up and she was blown against a stone sea-wall and stove in on one side. All her supplies had to be taken out while she was repaired. Meanwhile, her crew, having too little to do, proceeded to get drunk. Citizens of La Rochelle were sober, God-fearing people who allowed no disorder in their town. The crew were clapped into jail, and De Monts had a hard time getting them out again.

On the whole, the news from France was good. Although the king would not give his old friend the fur monopoly indefinitely, he graciously allowed his royal favor to be bought for one year — at a high price, of course.

There were new colonists from France — among them,

a young lawyer named Marc Lescarbot. While waiting for the *Jonas* to sail from La Rochelle, Marc had written a poem called "Farewell to France." So many copies were sold that the poem had to be printed again and again. Lescarbot had written poetry before, but never anything so popular.

"I was a lawyer," he told Champlain, "but my opponent bribed the judge, and my last case was decided against me. Such corruption is not to be endured, so I have given up the law and I have come to the New World to be a poet!"

Champlain looked the young man over. Marc was thin and pale, and his smooth white hands had never handled anything heavier than a quill pen. A poet is about the last thing we need here in the wilderness, thought Champlain. He took up a hoe and went out to work in his garden.

A few hours later, Champlain looked up in surprise. The poet was lustily swinging a mattox, rooting up the wild meadow grass, and making a garden of his own just across the brook. Marc worked all day. "France is full of beggars and vagabonds," he told Champlain. "It is because men will not stoop to till the soil, but try to make themselves gentlemen at the expense of others."

"Why — that's just what I believe!" exclaimed Champlain. He found himself liking this young man, after all. "Let me help you break ground," he offered.

Weeks passed, and Marc Lescarbot kept hard at work. His hands were bandaged because of blisters, and his back was sore, but he was always smiling and gay. "This noble toil was the pursuit of our first fathers, and of the kings of old," he announced, pausing to wipe the sweat out of his eyes.

A while ago, Champlain would have laughed to himself at such flowery language. Now, he had learned to appreciate the young man. "You need to rest," he suggested. "Come to my summer house to listen to the birds. Do you know, I think they like to see us there, and they sing the better just to give us pleasure. Afterwards, I will straighten that irrigation ditch of yours. You have made it crooked."

"Always measuring and surveying, aren't you —" laughed Lescarbot — "yet, stopping to feed the birds and to listen to their song! That's what I like about you — you're such a strange combination of the romantic and the practical."

The two men walked along the brook to the summer house and sat down in the cool shade. Sam had brought some bread which he crumbled on the ground for his birds. "I suppose you'll soon be off adventuring in one of those flimsy little ships your friend Champdoré builds," said Lescarbot. "How can you bear to leave this beautiful spot!"

"I have to map the coast for His Majesty," said Champlain in surprise. "That is my job."

"You mean you cannot resist the desire to see what lies just around the corner," laughed the poet.

"I suppose so," agreed Champlain. "Why don't you come with us and see how it feels to be the first white man to penetrate some mighty river."

But the young man wanted to stay in the settlement and work in his garden. "There is something you can do for me, then," suggested Champlain. "Keep up men's spirits with your gay songs. Get them out of doors to work with you in the fields. Then the scurvy will not come upon them while we are away."

"There are some men I cannot influence," said Lescarbot. "Those three or four boon companions from Paris may be sons of the nobility, but they are intent on drinking and throwing dice here in New France, just as they did back home."

"I know," scowled Champlain. "I have dealt with such ne'er-do-wells before. They are going on the expedition with us, and the discipline aboard ship should have a good effect."

But Sam said nothing of a matter which was troubling him deeply. Eustace Boullé, the boy who was like a younger brother, had taken to going around with these flashy fellows. These new-comers knew all the gossip of the court, the ribald songs, the latest slang. Eustace thought they were wonderful, and when they asked him to drink with them and join them in a game of cards, he was flattered to death.

15 · ARROWS THAT FLY BY NIGHT

THE SECOND expedition along the New England coast got
under way September fifth. The Sieur de Monts went
along, and so did the Baron de Pontgravé, and his son
Robert, who had come to America for the first time.

Off Cape Ann, the fog came down. "We must find a
safe harbor, or be wrecked by some hidden reef," cried
Champdoré, who had reason enough in his recent unhappy
experiences to make him nervous.

"On our last voyage, we passed the entrance to a harbor
not far from here," said Champlain. "There was not time
to explore it then, but I think I can find it for you now."

Sending for Daniel Haye, Champlain had the longboat
lowered. "Row slowly forward, Dan," he said, "while I
take soundings and watch the compass. Don't drop that
long rope that holds us to the pinnace, or we will lose each
other in the fog."

An hour later, the pinnace was safely anchored inside
Gloucester Harbor. "You see, before the fog came down,
I had found our position with my astrolabe," patiently
explained Champlain. Then he sighed. "Latitude, I can calculate, but I have never been able to contrive an accurate
way to find longitude. Sometimes I think God does not
want man to unlock this secret."

"The whole thing savors of black magic," muttered

Champdoré. "I'll have nothing to do with those mystic figures on that queer metal disk you call your astrolabe!"

"We're here safe and sound, at any rate," smiled Champlain. "Tomorrow, I shall be able to chart a new harbor."

But the morning sun revealed an alarming sight. Two hundred Indians swarmed along the shores of Gloucester Harbor in full war paint. "They mean mischief," said Champlain, studying the warriors through his telescope. "Look at the tomahawks — the quivers full of arrows! Well — let's see what a few presents will do."

"Here's an old coat of mine," suggested the Baron de Poutrincourt. "The gold lace is all tarnished, but the cloth is bright red."

"Just the thing for the chief!" agreed Champlain. Then he turned to Dan. "Get me a dozen trusty fellows, with muskets loaded, and we'll go ashore."

A war dance began as the longboat approached the beach. Taking the red coat, Champlain landed and walked straight to the chief, whom he recognized by the many eagles' feathers in his hair. One glance at this bright-colored coat was all the chief needed. He took it gravely, and put it on. Champlain gave a sigh of relief. Now all would be well.

But the chief was scowling. He took out his knife — and Sam exchanged a quick look with Dan which meant, "Watch out for trouble."

To everybody's amazement, the chief took off his new coat and began cutting it up. Then, with great ceremony, he presented pieces of it to his favorite followers. One got a sleeve, another, the collar — and soon, all the head men of the tribe were strutting about, wearing bits of Paris tailoring. Now Champlain dared not glance at Dan for fear of laughing.

On leaving Gloucester Harbor, the explorers followed the New England coast as far as Brant Point, a little north of Plymouth. Here, they tried to cut across Cape Cod Bay, but underestimated the extent of the cape and ended up in Wellfleet Harbor with a broken rudder! Champlain was exasperated. The expedition had started late in the season, and now they were still within previously explored territory. Daily, the winds grew stronger and the weather more unsettled. Somehow, they limped around the cape and repaired the damage at Chatham, on the eastern shore. Here, five or six hundred Indians had the largest town Champlain had yet seen.

With his usual friendly interest, Sam visited the Indians, asked questions by sign language and learned all he could of their ways. His was the first authentic account of North American Indians to reach European people, and today antiquarians marvel at the accuracy of his observations.

These Massachusetts Indians were living in lofty, circular huts, covered with matting made of grass or cornhusks. Inside, there was no furniture except a bed or two, raised a foot from the ground and made of cut saplings placed close together. For a mattress, the Indians used a reed mat "two or three fingers deep." Champlain did not stay inside the Indian huts very long, for the fleas were terrible. Fleas jumped on him and bit him even out in the fields while he was admiring the Indian corn!

Chatham Port and Pleasant Bay are delightful places to pass sunny October days, and while the repair work on the rudder went forward, the explorers rested and stretched their legs on shore. One rule, however, was strictly enforced — everyone must be back on the pinnace by nightfall.

Eight or nine days went by, and then the Baron de Poutrincourt brought disquieting news. He sought out Champlain, who was at work on a chart in the little cabin where meals were served. "The Indians are taking down their huts and sending their women and children and all their goods inland," he reported.

Champlain looked up in consternation. "This means an attack!" he said. "They have no furs to trade — nothing but vegetables and tobacco. And we have given them all the knives and axes they will get — so they plan to take the rest of our trade goods by force."

"That's it exactly," agreed Poutrincourt, "but we can handle them if we are watchful. The cook has gone ashore with some men to bake bread. I'll warn him to return well before dark."

Just then, one of the gay young men from Paris came swaggering into the cabin. He and his friends had behaved fairly well — interested in new scenes on the voyage. Now they were beginning to be bored with it all, and this man was drunk, although it was only mid-morning. When warned of danger from the savages, he laughed scornfully. "Tell you what," he said, "I'm going to get some fellows and camp ashore all night."

One of his friends appeared at the cabin door. "Ho there, Du Val," cried the braggart, "what do you say if we make for the beach and sing and shout all night, with no one to tell us to pipe down? We'll show who's afraid of these Indians!"

"Steward," said Champlain, turning to the man in charge of supplies, "see that these gentlemen have no more to drink."

White with anger, the loud-mouthed youth made a lunge at Champlain, but something in the older man's level gaze stopped him. He subsided into a chair, muttering under his breath. The man named Du Val said nothing, but he gave Champlain a glance of bitter hatred.

Later on, Champlain came across Eustace Boullé, cleaning a fowling piece. "Eustace," he said, "promise me you will not stay ashore after dark. And keep away from that fellow downstairs in the cabin — he doesn't know when he has had enough to drink."

For a moment, Eustace forgot what a wise and good friend Champlain had always been. "Oh, we have fun!" he flashed out. "Don't be an old fogy."

Champlain invited Eustace to go ashore with him while he warned the baker that the Indians were in a dangerous mood. Dan was already waiting in the longboat. But Eustace refused — thinking he was being treated like a baby.

"That Paris chap plays the braggart," said Champlain to Dan, as they pulled for the shore. "The young fellows put too much faith in him." Behind them, another rowboat put out from the pinnace. Loud talk and laughter indicated that these were the young men in question, with their ring-leader. Champlain started to look for Eustace; then he turned away. If the boy he loved so well were there, he did not want to see.

Toward evening, the baker rowed a boatload of fresh bread out to the ship. "Is everyone safe aboard now?" asked Champlain, who had returned some time earlier. The baker looked scared. He swallowed as if about to say something, then changed his mind and hurried below, with just a mumbled "Yes, sir."

By the feeble light of a horn lantern, Champlain went over his notes on the width of the channel leading into Pleasant Bay. Then, with a tired sigh, he rolled into his bunk. He remembered that he had not seen Eustace all day. It was not like the boy to sulk. The next thing Champlain knew, he heard shouts and running feet on the deck overhead. Rushing up the ladder, he saw that several hours had passed and it was dawn. From the shore came frantic shouts. "Help! Save us!" cried French voices, hoarse with fear.

In an agony of impatience, Champlain watched the long-boat being lowered into the water. The moments seemed like hours. Men with torches were running up and down the deck, lighting slow-matches and bringing powder and ball for the heavy muskets. The boastful young man from Paris was nowhere to be seen, nor were his friends. Champlain looked about for Eustace Boullé. A terrible fear clutched at his heart — Eustace was not on deck, either, and it was all too easy to guess which members of the expedition were on shore, calling for help.

Those cries were fainter now, and for the first time, the French explorers heard the eerie, long-drawn sound of Indian war-whoops. Surely, animals or devils must be producing such sounds — not men! Champlain jumped into the boat, followed by Pontgravé, his son Robert, Hébert, a trumpeter — and Daniel Haye. They rowed like mad, but the boat grounded while it was still a musket-shot from shore. They sprang into the water, weapons held high. In the uncertain light, they could see about three hundred Indians in battle array. Cries for help still came from the direction of the stone oven that the baker had built on the beach. The rescuers splashed forward as fast as they could. "Fire!" shouted Pontgravé, the moment the Indians were within range.

"They ran helter-skelter at the sound of the guns," said Champlain, thankful from the bottom of his heart that these Indians had never faced the white man's weapon

before. There was little time for rejoicing, however. Close
at his side came a flash and a roar, as an arquebus exploded.
This time, Robert, son of Pontgravé, was the victim. "Leave
me," he groaned, as Champlain ran to help him. "We must
save those fellows by the oven. I have only hurt my hand."
But the wound was a grave one, for Robert Gravé lost
three fingers of his right hand.

Champlain advanced with the others. "Eustace!" he
found himself shouting. "Eustace, where are you?" He
stumbled, and saw that a dark form lay huddled on the
sand. The body was still warm, but the deep-buried shaft
of an arrow told the story. Champlain bent down. A young
Frenchman lay dead — but it was not Eustace Boullé.

By the bake oven lay the ringleader who had persuaded
his friends to disobey rules and spend the night ashore. He
had been brought down by an Indian tomahawk. His little
white dog had leaped upon his back, and both dog and
master were skewered to the earth with one powerfully
driven arrow. The "braggart," as Champlain called him,
had received a terrible punishment for his wrong-doing.

In the growing daylight Champlain returned wearily to
his ship. "Send sailors with spades to dig three graves," he
said. "We were able to save Du Val and one other man
who was badly wounded. The savages must have taken a
prisoner, for no one has seen Eustace Boullé."

"My older brother, I am here!"

Sam spun around, incredulous, at the sound of Eustace's
voice.

"They called me coward, but I did not disobey orders,"
said Eustace. Boylike, he had slept like a log through all

the excitement aboard ship. Now he was furious to discover that he had missed being a member of the rescue party.

When it came time to write the story of the five young men who went ashore, no one ever told the name of the "braggart" who was to blame. There was no need to disgrace an honorable family. But if the braggart's name was suppressed, another name comes down to us in history. In Champlain's journals and in the story Marc Lescarbot wrote, we find Daniel Haye spoken of as "A very brave man." The young man who was wounded by the savages died during the following winter from his injuries. Du Val was unhurt, but he continued in evil ways. Samuel de Champlain was to regret ever having saved this man's life!

Leaving Chatham Harbor, the explorers sailed on, along Cape Cod. They anchored at Hyannis Port, then finally made their way through the straits we call Woods Hole. To the south, they glimpsed Nantucket and Martha's Vineyard and the strong current running through Woods Hole made them think they had come upon a river. "We will name this river in honor of the Sieur de Champlain," suggested the explorers — for they were turning back now, and they knew that the geographer longed to go forward.

16 · "THE PAGEANT OF NEPTUNE"

CHAMPLAIN's voyage of discovery was at an end. Near Martha's Vineyard he had reluctantly turned back, passed what is now Boston Harbor and sailed for Port Royal once more. Stormy winds delayed the return trip again and again.

Back at Port Royal, those left behind grew uneasy. "What if our leaders have been killed by hostile Indians!" they whispered to one another. Fortunately they did not know how close they came to the truth.

"Suppose their ship has been wrecked and they have all been drowned! Let's steal the pinnace and get out of here. We could find a fishing vessel at Canso to take us back to France — Who wants to perish alone in this wilderness!"

Young Marc Lescarbot heard the murmurings and realized that something must be done. One night at supper, he pounded on the table for attention. "Fellow adventurers," he began in his favorite flowery style, "our leaders will return any day now."

Ignoring the silence that greeted this statement, Marc continued. "We must be prepared to receive the Sieur de Poutrincourt and the Sieur de Champlain and the rest of the company in proper style. I have written you a play. It is called 'The Pageant of Neptune,' and I assure you it is done in the latest Paris fashion. We will choose the cast now and start rehearsing at once.

"Where's the blacksmith? Oh, there you are, Raoul. I want you to be Father Neptune."

"Huh! Er — I mean, beg your pardon, sir?" The blacksmith was much embarrassed, but laughter was heard in the gloomy barnlike dining room for the first time in weeks. Marc's plan to cheer up the men was beginning to work.

"Why Raoul, who else has a great shaggy beard and a fine broad chest like yours?" he said. "God of the Sea you must be, and I will teach you your lines, myself."

"Eh! Lines?" muttered Raoul.

"Yes, my man. Fifty-eight lines of verse. What a part! But if you want a longer one, I'd be glad to oblige. You know I love nothing better than writing poetry."

"Oh no sir — God forbid!" protested the poor blacksmith amid much laughter. "Will I have to get into the ocean, sir? I can't swim, you know."

"Never fear, my Sea-God," laughed Lescarbot. "You will ride in your royal chariot — our old rowboat with gay trappings."

Everyone laughed and cheered and the blacksmith saw that he was to be Neptune, and no mistake. He made one last despairing effort. "How will Their Lordships know I'm a Sea-God? They'll just think poor old Raoul the blacksmith has lost his mind."

"Hark now, and I'll read off some of your lines," offered Lescarbot. "Quiet, everyone — here's what our good Raoul will say to the Sieur de Poutrincourt: —

"Stop, noble leader, take a look at me,
I am the god who often aided thee.
And if thou dost not know my name —
Ocean's the kingdom whence I came.
Saturn my father, who had children three,
I'm Neptune — Mighty Ruler of the Sea."

The workmen and soldiers in the dining room pounded the tables and roared their applause but the poor blacksmith could only moan. "Fifty-eight lines like that! I can never do it."

No one paid any attention to Raoul, and the casting went on amid much laughter and good-natured fooling. Marc had purposely written a part for everyone who could be induced to take one. There were six Tritons to pull Neptune's royal chariot, and each had a speech. Four young men were chosen to dress as Indians and recite French verses of considerable length. Those without parts were put to work making costumes and decorations.

The whole atmosphere of the Port Royal settlement changed from gloom to gayety. Instead of leaving their work to watch — with homesick longing — for a ship that never came — men practised the songs and went over the lines of their play.

> "Savage people of this land are we,
>   Come to do honor to the fleur-de-lis,"

muttered the baker, as he drew the brown loaves out of the brick oven.

"In my speech I talk about Cupid, although I'm supposed to be an Indian," said the baker's helper. "Do you think an Indian would know about Cupid?"

"Don't be a dolt," said the baker scornfully. "I guess our Monsieur Lescarbot knows the way to write a play. Cupids and heathen gods like Neptune are all the rage at the King's Court. Now get your lines like a good lad, and put expression in 'em, too."

At night after supper everyone gathered to sing their four-part song and go over their lines. The days slipped by, and now it was Marc Lescarbot who became anxious. The exploring party was at least two months overdue. To keep his cast occupied, he painted the coat of arms of Poutrincourt and De Monts on big slabs of wood, and had them mounted at the entrance to the fort. Everyone was sent to the woods for mountain laurel to decorate the gateway.

I can't keep the men amused much longer, thought Marc. It was November fourteenth, and he was hunting for a green cloak suitable to drape around poor Father Neptune, so the smith's great chest would not be too cold. There came a shout from the shore and Marc dashed outside the fort to find an Indian running up the path.

"Look, look! The Sagamore Champlain is coming!" shouted the Indian.

Everyone ran to the shore, but the great Port Royal Harbor was empty as far as one could see. Finally the baker, who was very far-sighted, cried out that he saw a sail. What eyes those Indians had, thought everyone, when some minutes later the other settlers caught sight of a tiny dot.

It would be a long time before the boat could reach Port Royal but there was great excitement, even so. Everyone ran up and down, getting in each other's way, and all six Tritons declared they had lost some important part of their costumes. Father Neptune had such an attack of stage fright that he could not be gotten into his royal chariot till Lescarbot gave him a good drink of cider.

Aboard the incoming ship, Champlain and Poutrincourt could see people running up and down on shore, but they could make neither head nor tail of what went on. The explorers were weary after their long voyage. Provisions had run low, and they had two seriously wounded men. Now it looked as if the settlers at Port Royal had surely gone mad.

Then trumpets sounded. A gayly decorated boat put out from shore and in it sat a very nervous blacksmith holding a three-pronged fork! Champlain's weather-beaten face broke into a smile. "Upon my soul that's old Father Neptune, trident and all," he cried.

The rowboat came alongside: —

"Stop, noble leader, take a look at me,
I am the god who often aided thee — "

stammered the blacksmith, sure that Poutrincourt would order him arrested.

But the Sieur de Poutrincourt drew his sword and struck a mock-heroic attitude. Everyone laughed and clapped, so the blacksmith rumbled through his lines, only prompted now and then in loud whispers by one of the Tritons.

One after the other, the Tritons recited their verses. Poutrincourt had to put up his sword because his arm got tired. Finally it was the turn of the Sixth Triton, who said: —

> "Hurrah for Henry, Monarch of our Land,
> Under his laws the Savage Nations stand.
> Neptune will favor all the French so brave,
> Who cross to New France o'er his stormy wave."

Now came the "Savages" and even Biencourt smiled in spite of the pain of his mangled hand. The baker got on splendidly as "First Savage" and presented the explorers with a flank of moose meat at the end of his verses.

The "Second Savage," however, had rather a time using the gestures Lescarbot had taught him without upsetting the canoe.

> "Here is the hand, the arrow and the bow,
> Which gave this beaver his death-dealing blow,
> 'Twill make a splendid coat for thee,
> Highness, accept this gift of me."

The "Second Savage" just barely saved the beaver skin from falling in the water.

The "Fourth Savage" had the best part of all, and had

been chosen for his ability to play comedy. He pulled a long face as he approached the pinnace. In one hand he carried a fish spear; the other hand was noticeably empty. He spoke in the wheedling tone of an artful beggar: —

> "Sagamore, pardon if I come,
> With empty hands and sorry face.
> Good fortune only follows some,
> I was unlucky in the chase.
> Following Diana in my youth,
> Much game I got as I could wish.
> She's turned against me now, in truth,
> May Neptune help me catch a fish!"

He peered over the edge of his canoe as if looking for fish, then he shook his head dolefully and went on with his verses: —

> "Someday I'll catch one, who can tell?
> Meanwhile inside your boat I see,
> Some of that bread I like so well.
> Please to supply my tribe and me!"

The Fourth Savage came to the point with a delightfully crafty look, peering into the explorers' ship as though to make sure of getting all the bread they had. How many times Champlain had been approached with just such a modest request! He laughed long and loud, as did all the rest.

Trumpets sounded a fanfare and the cannon boomed from the fort as the leaders were escorted ashore. Port Royal was a wonderful place for echoes, and the hills gave back the sound of cannon for minutes at a time.

Once inside the hall, a last verse awaited the explorers.
Lescarbot himself recited these lines: —

"After looking in vain, Sirs, we see you once more.
The heavens are brighter since you came ashore.
Give a cheer all you butchers, you waiters and such,
Scullions and bakers, don't loiter so much.
Turn your pans topsy-turvy, your kitchen resign,
Only pour for our leaders a quart of good wine.

Cooks, where are the ducks? Let them turn on the spit.
Get chickens. The fat goose, good heavens, where's it!
Now enter companions. You're welcome indeed,
Boy hurry, to bring us the wine with all speed.
But first, before drinking let everyone sneeze,
So you smell the good dinner with never a wheeze!"

The banquet was all and more than the poem promised.
Afterwards the dining hall rang with men's voices as they
sang again the new song from Marc Lescarbot's pageant: —

"Good Neptune, grant us every one
Safety at sea. Thy waves command
To bear us on until we come
Home to our own beloved Land."

They sang this song more than once as the long winter
passed at Port Royal.

17 · THE ORDER OF GOOD CHEER

ONE EVENING CHAMPLAIN saw a light burning late in Lescarbot's window. He knocked, and Marc came to the door, a quill pen stuck behind his ear, and a smudge of ink on the end of his nose. "I hope I am not interrupting you in the midst of some immortal poem," said Champlain.

The poet laughed. "The Goddess of Poetry has fled to her home on Mount Parnassus. She was insulted by the lightness of my verses for the Neptune pageant."

"In that case, she is behaving very badly, for those poems were among your best," replied Champlain, seating himself before the fire. "You kept up the courage of your companions, Marc, and you cheered our expedition when we returned. Now the Sieur de Monts has gone back to France, leaving Poutrincourt in charge. He asks our help, and the question is, how can we keep up the good work?"

"Don't tell me I'm to stage a pageant every day!" cried Marc, in mock distress.

Champlain laughed. "You've done your share. But if we are to keep men from dying of scurvy, we must see that they eat well. No one must mope in his room, nibbling on crackers and salt beef, day after day."

"You can't order men to eat," objected Lescarbot.

"No, but we can invite them. I propose that we make a festival of every midday meal. Suppose we appoint a chief steward, whose duty is to provide fresh game and fish for our table. The steward might hold office for a fortnight — then it would be another's turn."

"Splendid!" cried Lescarbot. "My patron, the Sieur de Poutrincourt, has brought along his gamekeeper from his country estate in France. Already, the fellow is blood brother to the Indian hunters. Together they will find a deer if there is one within twenty leagues."

"Then the Baron shall be our first steward," proposed Champlain. "Now let me think — the office of chief steward will be a lot of trouble. We can't have people refusing, so I'll tell you what we'll do. I have a gold chain which I brought home from Spain. It shall be the badge of honor, and I will place it solemnly about the neck of our first steward."

"Yes, yes, I see it all!" Lescarbot was enthusiastic. "At the end of two weeks the chain of office passes to the next in turn. The old steward pledges the new man with a goblet of wine, while we all shout and cheer." Lescarbot laughed delightedly. "Then of course, the new steward will try to outdo his predecessor, and we will eat toasted beavers' tails, broiled salmon or roast moose every day!"

"I depend on you to contrive ceremonies, Marc," Champlain suggested. "We must have processions and songs — you know how to do it. Now for a name: 'The Order of Good Cheer' — how's that?"

"Exactly right," agreed Lescarbot. "A knightly order, we will be — such as Good King Arthur had of old."

"This will appeal mightily to a fine, high-spirited boy like Eustace Boullé," mused Champlain. "I will make him my squire, and he shall become a knight as soon as he really distinguishes himself in the hunt. But how shall we get everyone to take part? Some of our settlers cannot be trusted with a fowling piece, lest they shoot themselves or their friends!"

"Leave that to me," promised Lescarbot. "Our dining hall should be decorated every day. I'll soon have the most hopeless city dweller out scouring the countryside for sweet-smelling balsam boughs and laurel."

The Order of Good Cheer was started at once, and proved a tremendous success. "We ate as well as anyone could on the Street of the Bears, in Paris," declared Lescarbot. "Only it was much cheaper," he added, remembering the prices charged at those famous restaurants when he was there, back in 1605 or so.

"At our midday meal, the ruler of the feast, having had everything prepared by the cook, marched in, napkin on shoulder and wand of office in hand. Around his neck glittered the collar of the Order, which was worth more than four crowns, and after him marched all members of the Order, each carrying a dish." Lescarbot kept his word and organized entertainment for everyone.

Before long, all the Indians on the peninsula of Nova Scotia heard about the Order of Good Cheer and flocked to Port Royal. There was nothing they loved better than ceremonies — especially if there was food. "We were glad to see them," said Lescarbot, "and bread was given them as one would to the poor."

While ordinary tribesmen were given bread, Membertou, the old chief, was invited to sit at table with Champlain and the rest. This delighted the old man so much that he swore to protect the French if a hostile tribe should ever attack them. Some said that this enthusiasm would last only while there was free food, but Membertou proved to be a staunch friend as long as he lived.

Spring came early to Port Royal, and thanks to the efforts of Champlain and Lescarbot, only seven settlers died of scurvy. These men were "either downcast or slothful," Marc said, and he thought that if the settlers had been allowed to bring wives and children to work side by side with them, the colony might have prospered even better.

By March, everyone was out in the gardens getting ready to plant, and by May, the seeds were in the ground. The warm sun brought on such a wave of optimism that several settlers planted orange and lemon seeds!

All winter, the settlers had enjoyed delicious fish; and now that spring was here, they were simply swamped with them! "The smelt is the first fish to present himself," said

Marc. After that, the procession was endless till, finally, the salmon arrived, and broke the settlers' nets. What a fine country we have found, thought Champlain. Next year we can live here entirely independent of provision ships from France.

On the twenty-fourth of May a sail was sighted. "It was the hour when we had made our solemn prayers to God and distributed breakfast to the people," said Marc. The cannon boomed and trumpets sounded to welcome the ship from home. But the news aboard was disastrous.

Dutch traders, led by a French traitor, had carried off all the furs at Tadoussac. Not an Indian on the St. Lawrence River had another pelt to trade, and the Sieur de Monts was ruined. He could not spare enough money for the colony at Port Royal, even though one more year would make the place self-supporting.

Refusing to admit defeat, the Baron de Poutrincourt proposed to go back to France. He was a very wealthy man; perhaps he could raise funds to carry on the colony and persuade new people to try their fortune in Nova Scotia. His son, Biencourt, agreed to remain almost alone at Port Royal, and the faithful Membertou promised to look after him. "We must interest people in New France by showing some of the products of this wonderfully fertile country," said Poutrincourt. Several barrels of herring or sardines were salted, to take to France. The settlers scattered through the woods, digging up ground nuts, for the Indians had taught them to eat these pear-shaped roots of the wild bean. They proved so popular that they were grown in France, and street criers sold them, calling them "Canada."

Marc Lescarbot carried home some gum from spruce and fir trees, for he loved the delicious piney odor. He gave some to Paris churches, and it was used as incense.

Of course Indian tobacco went back to France, where it was becoming more and more popular. Neither Champlain nor Lescarbot cared for smoking, and Marc was very severe in his opinion of it. "Our Frenchmen who frequent the Indians are for the most part so bewitched with this tobacco," he said, "that they can no more be without it than without meat or drink, and upon it they spend their good money." It did not occur to anyone, even to the foresighted Champlain, that here was a new source of wealth from the New World.

By the eleventh of August, ships had left Port Royal taking almost every settler. Now the fish in Champlain's pool would never be caught, and no one would come to his summer house to listen to the birds. The wilderness would soon take over all the gardens. "What are you going to do now?" asked Marc, as the two friends walked the pleasant paths together for the last time.

Champlain was already looking ahead. "New France is bigger and more important than Port Royal," he said. "I am going back to Paris to ask the king for men and provisions to explore the St. Lawrence River."

"There is no money in it — the king will not listen."

"Suppose I make friends with Indian tribes far up the St. Lawrence and get them to bring more and finer furs?

Suppose we build a fort to keep off all the other traders?" countered Champlain.

"That is the kind of talk to please Henry the Great," agreed Lescarbot.

They walked slowly back to the settlement, and stopped at the house which Champlain shared with Baron Poutrincourt. "My map is almost finished," said Champlain. "Let me show you something that will interest His Majesty." They went inside and there, on a rough-hewn table, lay a large parchment. Champlain took up a quill pen and pointed to the still unknown Upper St. Lawrence. "Somewhere in this direction lies the Pacific. What would King Henry say to a French explorer who offered to find a northwest passage to India?"

Lescarbot bent over the map. "This River of Canada — you have not drawn the end of it."

"Suppose the St. Lawrence is not a river, but a strait!" Champlain's voice deepened with enthusiasm. "Or suppose it is a river, but there are lakes and other rivers to carry me forward. Someday the forest will open, and I shall look upon the Western Sea — the Pacific."

"You will persuade the king to send you journeying," Lescarbot said. "None could withstand such ardor — such faith — as yours."

"Join my expedition, Marc. Don't you want to see that blue horizon?"

For a moment the poet was almost persuaded, but he thought of hostile Indians and dangerous rapids. Lescarbot was no man of action, but he went back to his room and wrote a sonnet to the friend he could not follow.

Sonnet to Champlain

A king of Africa, in days of old,
Once sought the sources of the River Nile,
Through Libya's wearying land for many a mile.
So thou, Champlain, with this example bold,
Dost labor on for days and days untold
To map the mighty rivers of this isle,
Which thunder forth in such a fearsome style
And join the sea in floods of icy cold.
What countless honors will increase thy fame,
If one more river thou canst now ascend,
What luster added to thy well-known name,
If thou canst reach this noble goal someday!
So seek and find the endless river's end.
So lead all France at last to far Cathay.

Champlain was pleased, though rather embarrassed, to have a sonnet written about him. He would have preferred the companionship of Marc on his journey.

Back in Paris, Pontgravé and De Monts worked tooth and nail to keep their exclusive fur-trading rights. Other merchants fought against them in the law courts, and the best they could get was one year's monopoly.

This mad scramble for wealth concerned Champlain not at all. He asked only to serve his country, and Henry IV gave him sole authority to choose a site for a fort on the St. Lawrence. Surrounded by greedy self-seekers, the king recognized a man he could trust. "You will be in command of this fort, and second to De Monts in authority over the whole expedition," he said. "I see you still carry a long sword."

In the spring of 1608, two ships prepared to sail for New France. The Sieur de Pontgravé was in charge of one, De Monts and Champlain went aboard the other. But Pontgravé was ready first, and he sailed eight days before his friends. "Hurry," urged the Sieur de Monts. "Suppose the Dutch should take all the furs again — we would end in a debtors' prison."

On the third of June, De Monts arrived at Tadoussac and Champlain got into the longboat to go ashore for news. There was news indeed! Two Spanish ships had arrived at Tadoussac just before the Sieur de Pontgravé got there. They opened fire on the French, wounding Pontgravé and taking him prisoner.

"To arms!" shouted De Monts, as soon as Champlain told him what had happened.

"Now wait," counseled Champlain. "The Spanish have two ships of their own, and Pontgravé's vessel as well. That's three against one. I have come for my parchments proving I am the king's commissioner. Let us negotiate."

The Spaniards were only privateers out for easy pickings, and when they saw the hand and seal of the King of France, they lost their nerve. Champlain assured them that they must come to terms or involve their two nations in war. They signed the written agreement, and Pontgravé was set free, stolen furs returned and the Spanish promised to leave French territory.

The king will enjoy this story, thought Champlain, watching the Spaniards sail meekly away without firing a shot. But we must build a fort on the St. Lawrence with all speed.

18 · THE MURDER PLOT

To Champlain, sailing up the St. Lawrence River in his little skiff was like coming home. The faithful Dan was once more by his side, and together they scrutinized every likely spot where the new colony might be located.

On July 3, 1608, Champlain landed at a meadow at the foot of a high cliff. Five years ago, when he saw it for the first time, this place had fired Sam's imagination. Now he liked it better still. "I've mapped many a Spanish stronghold," he told Dan. "Never have I laid eyes on a place better suited for defense than this. 'Quebec,' or 'Place of Narrow Waters,' the savages call it."

"I think you meant to come here all along," suggested Dan, his eyes twinkling.

"I hoped to find a spot nearer Tadoussac," Champlain explained. "But Quebec is the one perfect place for a fort and a town. Go back to Tadoussac, Dan, and ask the Sieur de Monts to send workmen and supplies."

The river was too swift for the heavy wooden ships from France, however. Skiffs had to be built on the shore of the St. Lawrence, many miles below the site of the new colony. And even after the skiffs were ready, it was a tedious business getting stores up-river. Dan was put in charge of this work, with four or five good men under his command.

Surveying and drawing plans for the colony kept Champlain hard at work, night and day. First came the storehouse — most important of all buildings if the settlers were not to starve. It had a deep cellar and a good oak shingle roof. Then the *habitation*, as Champlain called it, was built as a headquarters for leaders of the colony. This was really a small fort, with loopholes for muskets on the ground floor.

Champlain looked longingly at the high cliff and began cutting a winding road to the top, but the fort he meant to build up there would have to wait. Right now, reasonably comfortable shelters must be built for all the men, and Champlain knew he was engaged in a grim race with winter.

"Let's take a holiday and go hunting," proposed some of the men who were new to Canada.

"There'll be time enough for that," Champlain told them. "Till snow flies — keep hard at work."

The young man by the name of Du Val, who had been

the sole survivor of the Indian attack at Nauset Harbor, was again with Champlain. He had learned nothing from that narrow escape from death. Now he encouraged the men to grumble, as they hacked down great oak trees and laboriously sawed planks for their future homes. "Champlain is killing us with work," he said. "We ought not to stand for it."

One night, Champlain flung himself exhausted on his rough bed of pine boughs. He would sleep for an hour or two — then rouse himself to go on with his drawings for the palisade.

But Du Val stole out of the half-built *habitation* and made his way to a small campfire which flickered on the bank of the river. Here, four workmen were gathered, the most evil men the French king ever sent from prison to handicap the efforts of a colony! "There is a Spanish ship in this river," whispered Du Val. And the four cut-throats gathered close to hear the news.

"Now swear to me not to breathe a word, and I will tell you how we can all become rich!" Du Val did not need to make this offer twice. The men's eyes glittered with greed as they promised, and Du Val continued. "All we need to do is to kill the Sieur de Champlain. When he is out of the way, we hand over Quebec to the Spanish and live like princes for the rest of our lives. I know how to get in touch with the Spaniards, and their offer is backed up with gold." He pulled out some bottles of wine he had stolen from the storehouse, and the men drank to their future wealth.

"Champlain is a very powerful chap," said one of the men. "How do you propose to do away with him?"

"Easy," said Du Val. "First, we get every man in the colony on our side. Here's how we do it — we take each fellow aside separately and promise to make him rich. He agrees — who wouldn't? Then we tell him to lie low till we dispose of Champlain, and if he doesn't like the idea, we slit his throat then and there. If anyone asks questions — the savages did it."

"That will take care of any man around here," said one jailbird.

"Wait — " objected another — "you can't deal with Daniel Haye so easily. He's as handy with a knife as the best of us, and he'd die defending Champlain."

"I know it," said Du Val sourly. "That part is all worked out, my friend. Haye goes to Tadoussac tomorrow, taking with him the only men who might have courage to upset our plans. Four days from now, we act."

The men took another pull at the bottles to signify their approval of the plans. "The five of us will have every fellow in this settlement living in fear of death," boasted one. Then he paused. "Er — you will finish off Champlain yourself — eh, Du Val?"

"Not at all!" said Du Val sharply. "Here is what we must do. Champlain goes to the forest each day to select trees for the palisade. None will do but the largest and hardest for us to cut, but never mind. Work like the slaves he thinks you are, for three days. On the fourth day, we five will meet him in the forest, strangle him — and we are free."

The men looked at each other. "It's no good," they

grumbled. "Anything could happen. Champlain never goes about unarmed, and he's quick on the trigger."

"We'd be five to one," urged Du Val.

But the men sullenly refused this plan, and Du Val saw that he must think of another. Just then, a candle gleamed out from the *habitation*. Champlain was awake and at work again. Because of family connections, Du Val ranked among the leaders of the expedition, and he was supposed to be asleep at colony headquarters. He got up hastily. "I'll see you tomorrow night," he promised his cutthroat gang. "Be sure I'll find a way to kill Champlain — without the slightest danger to ourselves."

Du Val approached the *habitation* silently, keeping in the darkest shadows. But the ground was strewn with chunks of wood, planks and piles of stone — all the clutter that goes with building activities. He struck his foot against a pile of iron chain which gave forth a subdued chink, just outside Champlain's door. Instantly, a stern voice called out — "Who goes there?" And Du Val saw his leader spring to his feet, loaded pistol in hand.

"It's me — Du Val," said the young man hastily. He lounged into the room, putting as bold a face as possible on his behavior. "I couldn't sleep, so I went out for a turn or two under the stars."

"Well, don't go wandering around in the dark without making yourself known," said Champlain sharply. "We have no idea how friendly the savages really are around here, and if I hear the slightest disturbance at night, I shall shoot first and ask questions afterwards."

"Quite right, sir, I'll be careful," said Du Val with pretended courtesy. But his black eyes smoldered with sudden triumph, for he had thought of the way to kill the man to whom he spoke.

Next night, Du Val whispered with his gang. "We will fake an alarm," he told them. " 'Savages!' we will shout — and Champlain will rush out, arquebus in hand. From a dark shadow, a shot brings him down. Accident — you see?"

Du Val agreed to fire the fatal shot, and his gang were delighted with the plan, especially as they had nothing to do but create a disturbance in the night.

"Good-by, Dan — hurry back," said Champlain, as his only friends set out for Tadoussac, over a hundred miles away. He was aware of sullen looks among the men left behind — but unless they were to freeze to death during the coming winter, the work must go on.

Three days passed. "I have sent word to the Spanish," whispered Du Val. "They are ready with the gold." Now the Sieur de Champlain had only one more day to live.

But on the morning of the fourth day a boat unexpectedly arrived from Tadoussac. While she was unloading, Captain Tait the pilot came to Champlain, who was digging in his garden. "Sir," he whispered, "your men are plotting to kill you."

Sam went right on turning over the rich soil, without missing a stroke of the mattock. "What have you learned?" he asked in a low voice. "Here — take the shovel and work along with me, so we will not appear to be talking together."

"I was astounded," murmured Captain Tait. "Natal the locksmith just told me, and begged me to warn you — although he expects a knife in his ribs if we are overheard. Tonight is the time, and midnight is the hour."

Rapidly, the pilot went over the details of the plot. "The scheme is well thought out — " nodded Champlain — "I believe it would have worked." For a moment a wave of loneliness went over him, for he had always been a popular leader, and it was hard to face the fact that his men were against him now. But the locksmith was braving threats to his life, to give the warning — perhaps others were under threat, as well.

Sam turned to the captain with a confident smile. "Let *us* plot, also," he said. "We are outnumbered, but if you have any good men aboard your boat, we can outwit these conspirators."

"My sailors are fine, trustworthy men," assured Captain Tait.

"Then choose me a young fellow who can play a part. I will give him three bottles of fine burgundy, and he is to hunt up the ringleaders of the plot. Have him tell them the wine was given him at Tadoussac, and that he wants some good companions to share it with him — aboard ship."

"I will tell my sailor lad to usurp my cabin, and then I will come ashore," contributed the pilot. "I will be armed — because of Indians, of course."

"The men were told to hurry with the unloading so that you could sail this afternoon," remembered Champlain.

"Never mind — I will give it out that the boat needs caulking." The pilot straightened, stretched his arms as though tired of work, and sauntered away across the garden. Half an hour later, Champlain followed.

At nightfall, Du Val and his ruffians sneaked aboard the pinnace with a very innocent-looking young man. The wine was mellow and good. They had finished most of it and were in the midst of a rousing song, when a stern figure appeared at the door of the cabin. "You are under arrest," said the Sieur de Champlain, backing up his orders with a heavy silver-mounted pistol. The ringleaders were soon bound with ropes by armed seamen, who only awaited the signal. Champlain returned to the *habitation*, where he had every man routed out of bed and brought before him. They stood shivering and blinking in the candlelight, while he told them the plot was discovered and the leaders arrested. "I forgave them all," he said, "on condition that they should tell the truth about everything that happened.

"Next day, I received their depositions, one after the other, in the presence of the pilot. They were glad, they said, for they were living in constant fear of one another and of the scoundrels who misled them. According to their statement, they were satisfied with the treatment accorded them, and they have lived in peace ever since."

All the ringleaders were handcuffed. They promptly accused each other, and even the surgeon of the settlement, who was able to clear himself at once. On one point, all the scoundrels agreed — Du Val, it was, who planned everything, even to delivering his country's fortifications to an enemy power. He was hanged at Quebec, and in accordance with the custom of the times, his head was set upon a pike on the highest part of the fort. So ended the life of this worthless young adventurer.

Heavy snows came early to the colony at Quebec, but

thanks to the experience of Champlain, the settlers pulled through in good shape. From the very first, supplies were carefully rationed and Daniel Haye guarded them like a dragon, lest selfish people should take more than their share. When starving tribes of Indians came asking for help, Champlain managed to spare a little corn for their children.

The savages promptly settled down just outside the palisade gates. Sam's heart was touched by the hardships the fierce Iroquois had brought to these weaker tribes who came to him in desperation. "The whole time they were with us," he said, "they were in such constant fear of their enemies that they often took fright in the night at their dreams, and would send their wives and children to our fort, while I opened the gates for them."

But if Champlain was kind, he was also careful. "One must not trust these people too far," he warned. The men of the tribe were never allowed inside the fort at night, nor could they come with their weapons by day.

Pontgravé cared nothing for Indians — unless they came bringing furs. He scoffed at Champlain's attempts to help starving tribes, but when spring came, Champlain reaped his reward. "If the White Father would journey up the long river — come — we will show the way." So said the grateful tribe that had been kept alive at the gates of Quebec.

Joyfully, Champlain set out; but hardly a day's journey from Quebec, he turned back! A large tribe of northern Hurons and some Algonquins met the explorer with fifty canoes. It seemed that during the previous autumn, brother tribesmen had caught eels and dried them near Quebec. Then they had given the eels to Champlain for safekeeping. When January came, they had asked for their eels and had gotten them back, all safe and sound. Now the whole tribe had come to see the White Father, the Guardian of Dried Eels!

"First, you actually store away those disgusting eels, and now you give up an exploration!" exclaimed Pontgravé.

But Samuel de Champlain knew what he was about. At his own expense he provided a three-day feast for several hundred unexpected guests. He gravely smoked the peace pipe and watched the ceremonial dances. In the end Pontgravé saw that he had laughed too soon, for the chiefs presented Champlain with two hundred beaver skins. These were not trade pelts, but treaty furs — the most beautiful of the winter's catch.

Although he did not realize it, Champlain was laying the foundation for considerable personal wealth. But to him, exploration was more important. "If I guarantee to protect you, will you lead me into Iroquois country?" he asked his Huron and Algonquin friends.

They answered him with a mighty shout. Already, they were on the war path, and if the white chief would bring his magic weapons, they would lead him deep among the Iroquois. Only let the fire-breathing stick called the gun thunder forth death to the enemy. Then, if he liked to make pictures of rivers and lakes, they were willing to humor him in what seemed to them a childish pastime.

19 · LAKE CHAMPLAIN

IT was decided to go exploring with the Indians — on their own terms. "If we teach these Iroquois a lesson, they will let the friendly Algonquins, Hurons and Montagnais trade with us in peace," reasoned Champlain.

"What could ignorant savages do against our guns and armor?" laughed Pontgravé's young son-in-law, De Marais, who was in New France for the first time. "Let me come along, De Champlain. We shall have great sport."

A considerable party traveled up the St. Lawrence. They marveled at the great width of the river at Lake St. Peter, but soon they heard the roar of waters as a swift current came tearing along among islands. A moment more, and their skiffs were flung about like chips. Wet to the skin and thoroughly frightened, De Marais turned back.

"Exploring the coast of Nova Scotia was a different matter," grumbled Pontgravé, lumbering along the riverbank in his heavy armor. "I prefer to discover new lands from the deck of a comfortable ship, and anyone who wants to bother to map the interior is welcome." He, too, gave up the adventure.

Consternation spread among the Indians as they saw their white allies turn back. They had reached the mouth of the Iroquois River, which flowed into the St. Lawrence from the south. The "Richelieu," we call it now, and it forms a water highway to fertile New York State. "This is enemy country," muttered the Hurons.

But Champlain urged them forward. "Three white chiefs are worth a regiment of less valiant warriors," he laughed, indicating Dan and Eustace Boullé, the only followers that remained at his side.

The war party now divided into three groups, with scouts ahead, the main body of men in the center and a hunting party well behind. The hunters supplied their men with food, but no frightened animals must go bolting across an Iroquois trail, to give away the secret advance of the strangers. At night, the Hurons built bark huts and surrounded themselves with palisades. Although most of them were equipped only with stone hatchets, this took but two hours, and Champlain marveled at their skill.

But when the palisade was completed, the whole party lay down to sleep inside it, without setting anyone to watch! In vain Champlain explained how to post sentries to warn of enemy approach. "We have worked enough," said the savages. "We cannot keep awake."

The tension increased as the war party moved deeper and deeper into Iroquois territory. Then one morning the river came to an end. Just ahead was a wide opening in the forest trees, and Champlain found himself facing a beautiful lake. The blue waters stretched on and on, till they were lost in mist, while on every side were delightful little islands covered with trees. "The savages told me — " breathed Champlain — "but I did not believe there could be such a lovely lake in all the world!"

Dan and Eustace smiled at each other over their leader's boyish enthusiasm. "This shall be called Lake Champlain," they cried.

To Champlain's disappointment, the war party traveled only at night from now on, lying hidden by day on one of the many thickly wooded islands. While the Indians slept, Sam worked at his rough draft of a map, and recorded their position as indicated by compass and astrolabe.

Everyone was surprised when they were able to travel the whole length of Lake Champlain without meeting a single Iroquois. They were almost at that strategic spot we know as Ticonderoga, and Champlain was told that beyond lay another, smaller lake — then, after a short march, a river flowed mile upon mile, until it reached the sea. How Champlain would have loved to map Lake George, and then, the Hudson! But an Iroquois village barred the way, right there at Ticonderoga.

"We will fall upon our enemies in the night," said the Huron chiefs. "Many scalps shall hang at our belts before we disappear into the forest. Back home in our own village, we will feast for many days."

This did not suit Champlain at all. "Why not just force them to let us pass and travel on?" he suggested. "I give you my word, no Iroquois can stop us, for my trusty arquebus will scatter them all."

The chiefs looked at the White Father as though he had lost his mind. "That is not how things are done," they explained patiently. "Surprise — then kill and run. That is the way to go on the warpath."

Then both Hurons and Iroquois were equally surprised one night about ten o'clock. Champlain and his savage friends were paddling their canoes not far from Crown Point when they came face to face with a band of Iroquois, also on the warpath! The two Indian tribes began shrieking and calling names, like rival gangs of small boys. Then the Iroquois recovered themselves sufficiently to make for the lake shore, where they began frantically building a barricade. For a while the Hurons stayed out on the lake, keeping their canoes together in the darkness by means of poles. Finally, they asked the Iroquois if they would like to wait for daylight before starting the fight! The Iroquois agreed, and the Hurons landed on an island and spent the rest of the night in war dances.

When dawn broke, the Hurons jumped into their canoes and advanced over the narrow strip of water that separated them from their enemies. They shouted insults all the way — "just as our soldiers do at the siege of a city," said

Champlain, remembering the campaigns he had fought under Henry of Navarre.

The Iroquois swarmed over the top of their barricade, thinking to catch the invaders at a disadvantage when they landed. Then, for the first time, the forest around Ticonderoga rang with the sound of gunfire. This gateway to the Hudson valley was the scene of many a battle in after years, but Champlain fired the first shot.

Sam had loaded his arquebus with four bullets, and he killed two men and wounded another with one shot! Then, from the woods, Dan's musket roared. He had landed below the barricade and slipped through the woods to attack the enemy's flank. Eustace fired from the other side, and the battle was practically over. The Iroquois were brave warriors, but they had never faced gunfire before. As the Hurons and Algonquins poured over the barricade, the enemy fled in confusion.

For three hours, the victors stayed on the lake shore, looting, dancing and feasting. Then, in spite of all Champlain could say, they headed back toward the St. Lawrence, taking ten or twelve prisoners with them. The three white explorers had to follow, since they could not go on alone.

After traveling about fifteen miles, the Indian allies stopped to torture their prisoners. This was new to Champlain, and he looked on with growing horror. When he tried to protest, the Indians said, "Iroquois did this to us and more, when our men were taken captive."

Finally, they allowed Champlain to shoot one prisoner whose sufferings were more than he could bear. They gave him a prisoner of his own, but they were shocked and

disgusted to see him treat this hated Iroquois with kindness. Champlain had always believed that the Indians could become Christians, but now he saw that the process of teaching them would be long and difficult.

At the Richelieu Rapids, the Algonquins went north to their homes, but the Hurons followed Champlain, making his return to Quebec a victory parade all the way down the river. He told them that soon he must sail away to visit the Great White Chief, Henry, back in France, and they presented him with gifts for the king.

According to Huron standards, the choicest item was the head of an Iroquois. Champlain thanked them politely, but he did not take it to the king. Instead, he carried a belt, most beautifully embroidered with dyed porcupine quills. The skins of two scarlet tanagers, the king also "deigned to accept" — as Champlain put it.

As usual, the interview with Henry IV was more like a friendly call than a royal audience. "The king took pleasure and satisfaction in my account of my travels," said Champlain. And the explorer was empowered to continue his work.

Champlain found that all was well with his colony at Quebec when he returned from France. The fur traders, however, were in a great state of mind. This year, they swarmed up the river in small boats, coming from Tadoussac to Quebec because no Indians had appeared to exchange priceless furs for cheap European trinkets. "These stubborn savages say they won't trade unless we protect them from their enemies," complained the traders.

"That seems reasonable enough," countered Champlain.

He learned that the Iroquois had built a barricade on the Richelieu River, where it empties into the St. Lawrence. Their plan of attack was simple. Just let the northern tribes appear with canoe-loads of furs, and the Iroquois would raid them, killing as many men as they could and carrying off the winter's catch of beaver skins.

As soon as Champlain appeared, the St. Lawrence tribes took heart. They agreed to attack the barricade, with their White Father and his men to help them. Sam of course counted on the traders to lend a hand.

Now the explorer discovered how difficult it was to lead savages in any kind of planned strategy. Champlain urged immediate, surprise attack but the Hurons and Algonquins held an all-night war dance instead. While the ceremonies were going on, the Iroquois struck! Algonquin scouts came running for Champlain, and he set out in a pinnace with five men and a pilot named Thibaut. "Come on," he shouted to several boatloads of traders who had followed him to Three Rivers. But these men had no interest in risking their lives. Instead, they turned tail and fled down the river.

Champlain paid no further attention to the cowards, but went forward with Captain Thibaut. About a quarter of a mile up the river, the Algonquin scouts beached their boat and took to the woods. They were soon out of sight. "We were loaded down with our pikemen's armour," said Champlain. "This bothered us greatly, and in a few minutes we were hopelessly lost!"

"We must turn back and make our way along the river," counseled the explorer. Just then he caught sight of two Algonquins. "Where is the fight?" he demanded. Evidently they knew, but had no intention of going anywhere near it. Champlain forced them at the point of his musket.

Before long they came out upon the Richelieu River. In front of them was a crude wall of logs, with dark forms struggling fiercely on both sides of it. Dawn was just coming, and the river gleamed with a cold, gray light. "As I was firing my first shot, close to the barricade, I was wounded by an arrow which split my ear and pierced my neck," said Champlain. "I seized the arrow, which was still in my neck, and pulled it out."

Plenty of Algonquins saw the casual way in which Champlain plucked out the arrow and tossed it aside — then reloaded his musket to fire again and again. This was the Spartan sort of bravery they admired most. Champlain became the great hero of their tribe.

But the battle was going none too well. The Iroquois had arrived in force, and had thrown their enemies into confusion by their early-morning sortie. Now they had been driven back behind the wall of logs, but there they fought with great bravery.

In the growing daylight Champlain noticed that the barricade was built of logs laid crosswise, held by only two or three upright pieces stuck in the river mud. "Run to the pinnace and get ropes," he ordered one of Thibaut's men.

When the ropes arrived, the sailors contrived to throw them over the upright logs. Many willing Algonquin braves heaved hard. Over went the supports and the log barricade came tumbling down.

With a mighty yell, the Algonquins swarmed over the

fallen logs. The Iroquois were thrown into confusion by the collapse of what they had believed to be a strong wall, and they fled. Many were killed, and triumphant Algonquin war cries rang through the forest.

"If only I had been there," groaned Daniel Haye, when he heard about the fight.

But Champlain smiled and shook his head. "Just clear your fields and build your cabin, Dan," he said. "Soon, you will have a home ready for that girl you told me about, back in Normandy. In the end, the building of homes is far more important than the fighting of wars, you know."

Now that the Iroquois had been driven away from the St. Lawrence, the northern tribes set out with their furs to Quebec. The traders were as brave as lions, since all danger was past. Champlain had to keep an eye on them, lest they cheat these friendly Indians and cause more trouble.

"I must ask the king for an adequate force of men to keep this trade route open," thought Champlain. And he felt sure His Majesty would see the importance of this move.

Then terrible news arrived from France. Henry IV had been assassinated! The king was riding alone in his gilded coach one Sunday afternoon. A collision between two carts in the Street of the Ironworkers held up the royal carriage. Henry leaned out to see what was the matter. In a doorway stood a great, red-bearded man, with a cloak over his arm. This man, whose name was Ravaillac, instantly identified the alert, vigorous face of the king, with its hawk nose and stiff, upstanding gray mustache. He leaped for the royal coach, wrenched open the door and whipped a knife out from under his cloak. Ravaillac plunged the keen blade into the king's heart.

No one knows what prompted this man to kill one of the greatest leaders France had ever had. Some believe that the evil queen, Marie de Medicis, contrived the murder of her husband. In any case, she tried to seize the power when her nine-year-old son became Louis XIII. The late king's brothers also tried to seize the power, and France was in a turmoil.

20 · LAKE HURON

CHAMPLAIN hurried back to France to see if he could find a new patron for his colony of Quebec. Savignon, son of an Algonquin chief, went along, and Étienne Brulé, follower of Champlain, remained with the tribe to learn their language. The Indians would think it only right to kill Étienne if anything happened to the son of their chief — so Savignon was a great responsibility. But he was a tall, handsome youth, and Champlain knew it would be good showmanship to rig him up in war paint and feathers, and present him at the court of the boy king.

"Champlain's Indian," they called Savignon in Paris.

Whenever he saw two men arguing in the street, he would run up to them and say, "Cowards! Why don't you fight?" And he would offer his knife and try to demonstrate the best way to cut a throat. Savignon was a great pet among the gay young men in Paris, but Champlain found him quite a problem.

Greed and suspicion had infected everyone at court, as Champlain soon saw. With relief, he turned to the home of Eustace Boullé, where he would find trustworthy friends. A servant showed him into the Boullés' drawing room, which seemed to be empty. Then something very like a stifled laugh made him turn.

At the window sat a young lady, all dressed in white. Her gown was built out at the hips in an enormous wheel-like arrangement called a farthingale, but her tiny waist was so tight she could hardly breathe.

"I beg your pardon, Mademoiselle," said Sam, with a polite bow. "I did not see you there, behind that embroidery frame." Then he took another look at the girl's laughing eyes and very young face. "By the Saints, it's little Hélène!" he exclaimed.

Eustace Boullé's sister rose and made a curtsy. "Welcome home, Sieur de Champlain," she said very formally. But she burst out laughing, in spite of herself. "You didn't know me, did you?" she cried. "I have grown up since you went away."

"In that case, I suppose you do not want to see if I have brought you a gift from New France," said Sam, pretending to hide a big leather pouch behind his back.

Hélène Boullé almost fell over her long skirts as she

ran to look in the pouch. She pulled out necklace after necklace of tiny purple or white shells, all stitched in intricate patterns on bands of leather. "How lovely!" she exclaimed. "Why, each is different, and I don't know which I like best!" She promptly heaped all the strings of wampum around her neck, where they looked rather strange along with the necklace of oriental pearls her father had given her.

At this point, Eustace arrived. "Well, did you play the great lady and is poor old Sam sighing his heart out for you?" he laughed.

"Oh, stop teasing, and see what Sam brought me."

But Eustace only laughed louder still. "That wampum is like gold to the Indians," he told his sister. "Girls your age are loaded down with it, so that Papa can make a good match for them. Ask Sam if you've got enough of a dowry around your neck so he'll marry you."

To Champlain's surprise, Hélène blushed and ran out of the room. "What's the matter?" he asked. "She never used to mind when we teased her."

Eustace was looking a little ashamed of himself. "I shouldn't have said that," he admitted. "You see, Hélène is really grown up now, and Father is going to arrange a marriage for her. Of course she will not be consulted about her future husband, but I rather suspect that she has set her heart on a certain national hero." Eustace clapped his friend on the back. "Remember what I've told you many times, Sam. She's a sweet little thing — you couldn't do better."

Adventure in far places had so filled Champlain's life

that he had never thought of marriage. Now, he saw that he had always cared a great deal for Hélène, even when he regarded her as a little sister. She had grown very beautiful now, and with a stirring of pulses, Champlain realized that this was the girl he hoped to marry! "I am going to ask your father to consider me as a possible son-in-law," he told Eustace.

Hélène's father had been secretary to King Henry IV, and he knew Champlain well. "You have never been over-influenced by money," he said bluntly. "Hélène's dowry amounts to more than a thousand pounds in gold, but I don't suppose you even knew that. I shall be happy to see my daughter married to a man I can trust — one who can take care of her in these troublous times."

On December 27, 1610, Nicholas Boullé, Secretary of the King's Chamber, signed the marriage contract with "The nobleman, Samuel de Champlain." The bride's signature was not required, and for a while she was to live with her parents. But little Hélène was Madame de Champlain now, and someday Sam would take her to that wonderful New France she had heard so much about.

Before going back to Quebec, Champlain asked his father-in-law for advice. "Who will help me to continue explorations and improve Canadian colonies?"

"A brother of the late king, Count Charles de Bourbon, will probably become Governor of Canada," said the Sieur de Boullé. "Beware of the queen. She tries to control everything — only to deliver us into the hands of Spanish Jesuit priests."

"I hear they are killing Protestants at Brouage again,"

said Champlain. "Some are members of the nobility, and a person does not know what to believe. We have lost our religious freedom guaranteed by King Henry, and it brings sorrow to true Frenchmen."

"Thank God you are a Catholic, and my daughter is now the wife of a Catholic," murmured the Sieur de Boullé. Champlain wondered why he turned so pale.

The trouble in France was making itself felt in faraway Quebec, when Champlain returned. The old fur company had been dissolved and a new one, headed by unscrupulous men, flooded the river with traders. Champlain was very angry when he discovered that guns and liquor were sometimes secretly sold to the Indians.

Once more, the Algonquins and Hurons refused to come down to Quebec with furs. Champlain set out to find them and discover the trouble. Behind him streamed the traders in their skiffs, like jackals following a lion.

They came to an island in the St. Lawrence, more than a hundred and fifty miles from Quebec. "Now here is just the place for a trading post," exclaimed Champlain. He named it "Isle de Sainte Hélène" in honor of his wife. Today, great bridges spring proudly across the river and this island is the site of the city of Montreal. Champlain climbed the mountain near by which we know as "Mount Royal."

Still no Indians appeared, and Champlain proposed traveling farther up-river. The traders refused. They knew they had been treating the Indians badly while Champlain was away, and now they feared an ambush. Leaving them all behind, Sam went forward with Savignon, his young Indian, a French youth named Louis and an Indian guide.

They camped by the great Lachine Rapids. Champlain preferred to watch the mighty roaring river from the shore, but Savignon, Louis and the guide went out in a canoe. Late in the afternoon Savignon came running to Champlain. He threw himself upon his knees in front of the explorer. "White Father, kill me," he cried. Then he began his death song.

"Stop that!" commanded Champlain sharply. "Tell me what has happened."

Savignon pointed to an overturned canoe, flung high on a rock in the middle of the river. "The guide said we could shoot the rapids from this side," he gasped. "I said no, but the French boy wanted to try. We struck a rock and went over. The guide clung to the canoe, but the river snatched it away and he went down. I, only, am safe. Kill me, White Father. The Frenchman was drowned first of all."

"No need to sing your death song, my boy," said Champlain. He saw that Savignon was bruised and bleeding, after being flung against the rocks in the terrible current. "My friend's death was an accident, and Christians do not demand a life for a life, as Indians do."

Next morning the Algonquins arrived. With them was Étienne Brulé, dressed like a Huron warrior. He had been treated as the chief's own son, but if Savignon had been drowned the previous day, the Hurons would have killed Étienne on the spot. Would they have stopped there? Champlain thought not. He sensed that they were in a dangerous mood.

"Men told us that our White Father was dead," said the

chief. He advanced and solemnly lifted Champlain's hair to expose his deeply scarred ear. Then he addressed the tribe. "Behold the man who was wounded in your defense!" he began. "My son he brings safe over many waters. Now who shall say that the White Father speaks with a double tongue!"

Champlain had learned enough of the Algonquin language to follow the chief's speech pretty closely. He was puzzled, but he said nothing, and continued to lay out a tempting display of gifts.

Later, Étienne Brulé explained. "Remember the Iroquois prisoner you saved from death, sir? While you were away, he escaped from Quebec with a fine load of goods he had stolen. Now he spreads the tale that those goods were a present for his chief. He says you plan to make allies of the Iroquois and betray all the St. Lawrence Indians."

"Now why should my Indian friends believe such lies?" exclaimed Champlain.

"Because of the greed of the traders," said Étienne. "They would betray their own brothers — and often do."

So the work of building confidence must be done over again! Champlain went freely among the Indians, and before long, the furs began to appear on the St. Lawrence again, and the traders flocked to the river. "They had all the profit — I, the risk," remarked Champlain.

But the Huron chief presented the explorer with a hundred beaver skins of finer quality than any trader could buy. Algonquins came with more beaver for the White Father, and also with an offer that meant more to him than

riches. "They promised to show me their country, even at the risk of their lives," Champlain said.

It was 1613, however, before Champlain was able to start on a long journey of exploration. By this time, he had met a young man by the name of Nicholas Vigneau, who was setting Paris agog with tales of New France. He had just spent a winter with the Hurons, and he swore under oath that he had traveled up the St. Lawrence and Ottawa Rivers to an inland sea. There, he said he had seen the wreck of an English ship and talked to an English boy who was a captive among the Indians.

Just the year before, Henry Hudson and eight of his men had been set adrift in Hudson's Bay. They were never heard of again, but the mutineers who did this wicked thing went back to England and published Hudson's maps. Champlain had seen them. Naturally, everything seemed to add up — Vigneau's story of the upper Ottawa — then Hudson's Bay — and then, of course, the Pacific Ocean. "I was delighted," said Champlain, for the Northwest Passage seemed to be just up the Ottawa River.

The Indian guides were not at all pleased with Champlain's proposed route. "We never use the Upper Ottawa," they said, "unless we are pursued by enemies." But they had promised to show the White Father the country, and they would guide him where he wished. Although the going was very bad, the country was beautiful. They came to a waterfall which sprang out over a cliff, leaving a space where men could pass dry-shod. "Rideau" or "Curtain" Falls, Champlain called it, because it seemed so strange to walk behind a curtain of green water.

Leaving the site of the modern city of Ottawa, the river swings northwest. A storm had brought down great trees, crisscross over the stream. "I was loaded only with three arquebuses, as many oars, my cloak and some little things," said Champlain cheerfully. "I encouraged my men, who found the mosquitoes a worse burden than their loads."

Perhaps one of the "little things" was Champlain's astrolabe, which he depended upon for finding their position by the stars. At Muskrat Lake, about seventy-five miles from the present location of Ottawa, the astrolabe disappeared. Champlain searched for it in vain, and from then on his map was somewhat less accurate. Almost three hundred years later a boy of fourteen picked up a queer bronze object on the shore of Muskrat Lake. There were strange figures, and the date — 1603. The boy had found Champlain's astrolabe, lost in 1613!

On leaving Muskrat Lake, Champlain journeyed ever northward. At last, at "Allumettes" or "Matches" Lake, the Indian guide refused to go farther. "But is not the Western Sea just ahead?" insisted Champlain.

The Indians shook their heads. There was no sea, nor even any great bay, but only a wilderness of lakes, and finally, deep snow. They turned fiercely to Nicholas Vigneau, who had been with Champlain all this time. Until now Vigneau had stuck to his story of following the Ottawa to Hudson's Bay. "Admit that you did no such thing," the savages said. "You spent a winter among us, but you never left our lodges. Admit you never saw a wrecked ship, English scalps or a captive boy!"

Champlain was watching Nicholas Vigneau's face, and

now he read the truth. He had been tricked. This man was a liar, and had led him far astray. Bitter disappointment had come to Champlain just when he thought he was on the threshold of success. "Never let me see your face again," he told Vigneau. And for the first time, he wrote in his journal, "I could not control my anger."

The savages cheerfully offered to kill Vigneau on the spot. They could not understand when Champlain refused. "Perhaps the White Father will believe his Indian friends," they said sorrowfully. And Sam remembered that the guides had insisted all along that Vigneau was lying.

Now for the first time, Champlain felt that the road ahead led nowhere after all. Then his Indian friends began to talk to him about lakes, so wide no man could see across them. At first Sam thought they were just making up tales. "Had they ever lied to the White Father?" they demanded.

Champlain had to admit that his white friends seemed to do most of the lying. In 1615, he went exploring with the Indians again. This time, they followed the Ottawa to Lake Nipissing. "Is this your great lake?" asked Champlain — ready to believe that it was, for Nipissing was fifty miles long.

The Indians looked scornful. "Wait!" they protested. Down the French River they paddled — then suddenly they were out upon beautiful Georgian Bay. "A great inland sea," Champlain called Lake Huron, which stretches onward for two hundred and fifty miles.

21 · LOST IN THE WOODS

IN THE early spring of 1615, Champlain had returned to Quebec with two Franciscan fathers from his own birthplace, Brouage. He left them at the *habitation* while he journeyed swiftly up the St. Lawrence to spread the news among the Indians, not only that trade goods had arrived from France, but that new friends had come to teach a new religion.

Out of the forest swarmed hundreds of savages with their wives and children. They gathered at the mouth of a little river just above Quebec and Father Denis and Father Joseph said mass, "with all devotion, before all those people." Champlain was happy as he saw his Indians "in admiration at the sight of the ceremonies used and the ornaments which seemed to them so beautiful, the like of which they had never seen."

Father Joseph wanted to go right out into the wilderness with some Hurons. Champlain warned him of the hard life to be endured but followers of St. Francis were not afraid of poverty. "I must live with these people if I am to save their souls," insisted Father Joseph. As Champlain set out with Algonquin warriors, Father Joseph was preparing for a journey of his own.

I wonder if I will ever see the good Father again, thought Champlain as he stood on the shores of Lake Huron. How I would love to show him this beautiful inland sea! Champlain would have liked to paddle due west across the lake but the Algonquins told him that too many enemies lay in that direction. "Let us go into Huron country — they are our friends," the Algonquins suggested.

So Champlain turned southeast along the shores of what we call Georgian Bay. They came to a palisaded Huron village, the largest they had yet seen. And there was Father Joseph, comfortably ensconced in a little cabin which the savages had built for him! A huge wooden cross stood near and Champlain attended mass for the second time in the wilderness. How strange it seemed to find the good priest as safe and contented as though he had been in a little French village back home!

Deeper into Huron country went Champlain and soon the scenes became less peaceful. An expedition against the Iroquois was being planned and both Hurons and Algon-

quins made it plain that Champlain must take part. This was the price he had to pay for permission to explore. They left Lake Huron and traveled to Lake Simcoe, which they crossed. Then on they went to Lake Ontario, hot on the trail of the enemy.

Now they dared travel only at night but Champlain was able to add one more great lake to his map. On the south shore of Lake Ontario, the Indians hid their canoes; then

they began to slip stealthily through the woods in the direction of Lake Oneida. Passing Oneida, they approached Lake Onondaga and now the war party had reached their objective.

The Iroquois town to be attacked was protected by a log palisade. Champlain told the Hurons that towns with stone walls around them were captured in France by means of a *cavalier*. This was a movable wooden tower. Soldiers approached walls under a *mantelet* or wooden shield big enough to protect several men.

The Hurons constructed a *cavalier* and *mantelets* without much trouble. But they had never been taught to act together like soldiers. The *cavalier*, they pushed up to the walls of the Iroquois town. It was high enough so that Champlain could fire his arquebus down into the gallery that ran behind the palisade. He cleared the defenders away from the walls, but then his Hurons got excited and forgot what they were to do next.

The Hurons were supposed to advance under *mantelets* and set fire to the walls. First, they forgot the shield — then they set the fire wrong, so that the wind put it out. In vain, Champlain shouted orders from the top of the *cavalier*. They couldn't hear and, before long, they ran out of firewood. Two of their chiefs were wounded, and so were fifteen warriors.

The next day a high wind arose — just the thing for setting fire to the town. But the Hurons wouldn't go back. They felt quite proud of what they had already done, and for four days they would neither advance nor retreat. Instead, they kept getting into skirmishes and having to be rescued by Champlain with his arquebus. Finally, Champlain was painfully wounded in the knee.

Now the Hurons were ready to retreat, and Champlain was all admiration for the way they took care of their wounded. Queer wicker baskets were quickly made and he found himself doubled up like a jack-knife and slung on the back of a strong warrior. Other wounded men were carried the same way at a swift pace through the forest, while a force of warriors guarded front, rear and wings of the column.

The retreat was very long — about eighty miles — and the doubled-up position in the basket was such agony that Champlain soon forced himself to walk. This seemed to be just the right treatment, for his knee grew well rapidly. Snow was falling by the time the Hurons reached their hidden canoes on the banks of Lake Ontario.

A surprise was in store for Champlain. He found that the savages had decided to keep him by Lake Huron all winter, in case the Iroquois might attack. They wanted that fearsome arquebus to speak, if their enemies came looking for revenge. With his usual cheerful philosophy, Champlain made the best of the situation. He joined in a deer hunt which was to provide the Hurons with meat for the winter.

First, the savages built a circular stockade having one narrow entrance. Then, beaters went out and drove deer into the pen. A hundred and fifty head were killed, and after a big feast, the winter meat was smoked and deer fat was stored away to be used like butter.

Champlain almost missed the feast, though. He saw a bird about as big as a hen, yellow all over except for its head, which was red! Naturally, Sam wanted to catch that bird, and off he went, but the bird led him deeper and deeper into the forest. It finally got away. When Sam tried to find his way back to the Indian village, he had no idea in which direction to turn.

Champlain liked to tell the story. "I lost my way in the forest, now going one way, now another — without being able to see where I was. As night was coming on, I passed it at the foot of a tall tree.

"The next day, I set out and walked until three o'clock in the afternoon, when I found a little stagnant pool and, seeing some game birds there, I killed three or four. Tired and worn out, I prepared to rest and cook these birds, from which I made a good meal.

"I prayed God to aid me in my misfortune in this wilderness, for during three days there was nothing but rain mingled with snow, and I caught no glimpse of any footprint except those of wild beasts. At dawn of the second day I resolved to find some brook and follow it, judging it must empty into the river where the hunters were.

"At noon, I found myself on the shore of a small lake where I killed some game which helped me very much, and I still had eight charges of powder. Walking along the shores of this lake, I found a larger brook, which I followed till five in the afternoon. Listening, I heard a great noise. It was a waterfall in the river that I was looking for!

"I saw an opening, and when I reached it, found myself in a very large, spacious meadow where there were a great many wild animals. On my right I saw the river, wide and big."

Champlain was still twenty miles away from the Indian camp, but next morning he took careful note of some distant mountains and decided to go upstream. How good it was, to see the broad patch of sky above the river, after the stifling forest! It was good to walk with assurance in the right direction, after blundering about among endless trees. Soon, he caught sight of the smoke of campfires.

The Indians were overjoyed when Champlain walked into camp. He admitted that he got scolded. "They had been searching for me and they begged me not to separate from them any more, and to take my compass, which I had forgotten, and which could have put me back on my way. They said to me, 'If you had not come and we could not have found you, we should not have gone to the French any more, for fear of their accusing us of taking your life!'"

During the winter Champlain could have reached Lake Superior if he had followed his own desire. Instead, he settled a fierce quarrel which broke out between Hurons and Algonquins, and this was the greater service to New France. A war among friendly tribes would have meant no furs at Quebec in the spring.

Living with the Indians could not be called luxury, but Champlain enjoyed what he could and learned about everything. When he was a boy back in Brouage, he was forever sticking his nose into old Babette's soup kettle and asking her what she had put in it to make it smell so good. Now, he asked the Indians what went into their kettles. "It is *migan*," they said. "You boil two or three handfuls of corn in an earthen pot. Then throw in fish — either fresh, or dried."

"Do you clean the fish?"

"Oh no —" The Indians looked puzzled. "Why bother?"

And Champlain smiled to himself. So that was why the soup smelled and tasted so very bad. "You can make *migan* with venison, too," he wrote in his notebook. "But that smells bad, also."

Indian children sometimes had a very special treat. "They take an ear of Indian corn, put it under water and under mud for two or three months, until it is putrid. I assure you, nothing smells so bad as this corn, as it comes out of the water all covered with mud; yet, the women and children take it and suck it like sugarcane, there being nothing they like better, as they plainly show."

When spring came, the Hurons proudly escorted Champlain to Quebec. He had been given up for dead, yet here he was, with more Indians ready to trade with the French.

The prosperity of his own colony, Quebec, was dear to Champlain's heart, and he fought for it against impossible odds. While he worked among the Indians, persuading them to trade, the people left behind at Quebec grew lazy and spent their time hunting and drinking. No sooner would Champlain restore order and industry in Quebec than he must cross the sea to straighten out some trouble in France. While he was in Europe Quebec always went to pieces and war broke out among the Indians.

It was not until 1620 that Champlain felt safe in bringing Hélène to New France. "I returned with my family," said Champlain proudly. And there at Tadoussac was Eustace! "My brother-in-law was greatly surprised to see his sister and to think she could have made up her mind to cross so stormy a sea. He was greatly pleased, and she and I still more so."

Champlain had discovered a strange thing about his wife. She was secretly a Protestant! So that was why her father looked so frightened when the persecution of Protestants began again. Perhaps that was why he was happy to see her safely married to a prominent Catholic gentleman.

But Sam was greatly distressed — not because of the danger, but because he truly thought his wife's soul would be lost. He took her hands gently — "Let me find someone like good Father Joseph to teach you," he begged. "How can I try to lead a Christian life on earth, knowing I shall not meet you in Heaven!"

If Sam cared so much, Hélène would not resist. She learned her lesson so well that, once in Quebec, she gathered little Indian children about her every day and taught them the catechism. Hélène wore a pretty mirror fastened to her waist by a chain. It was a new Paris fashion, and the Indian children never stopped marveling over it. When they saw their own faces in it, they whispered, "She keeps our souls in there!"

Some were frightened, but others said, "Don't worry. Can't you see she is a saint, just like the pictures at the house of the Holy Father? She will take our souls to Heaven someday." And they asked if there was plenty of moose meat in Heaven.

22 · WAR CLOUDS GATHERING

WHEN CHAMPLAIN arrived at Quebec with Hélène, he found everything falling to rack and ruin. The men he had left in charge were lazy and discipline was lax. "I had my king's commission read," he said. "Then I set everyone to work. The whole winter was spent repairing the factory and the adjoining houses, and fortifying them."

Champlain used the word "factory," but he did not mean a place where things are made. The factory was the warehouse where European goods were kept and where furs were stored until they could be taken to France.

Champlain had made friends with so many tribes of Indians that the warehouse was crammed with valuable pelts. They belonged to the fur company, but Sam was responsible for their safety. He thought how easily a shipload of Spaniards might creep up the river in shallops to plunder this wealth. Sam wrote to the king for more arms and men.

The first ship from France brought a letter from King Louis XIII. "Champlain, I have seen by your letter with what earnestness you are working at your settlement, and for the good of my service. Not only do I feel very thankful to you, but it will give me pleasure to recognize it to your advantage, when opportunity offers. Meanwhile, I have very readily granted some munitions of war."

With high hopes, Champlain awaited the loaded shallops from Tadoussac. They arrived, in the charge of a stranger by the name of De Caen. "You are to deliver over all the furs in the warehouse," this man said.

"That, I cannot do," replied Champlain. "The furs were bought and paid for by the Sieur de Pontgravé. You must show me a court order to prove that you are the head of a new fur company."

De Caen stamped and raged, like the unmannerly scoundrel that he was. When he saw that Champlain was not to be intimidated, he sailed back to France — but in revenge, he carried away over half the food supplies he was supposed to deliver to Quebec. "The savages brought us a fine lot of moose meat, or the settlement would have been badly off," said Sam.

When the arms and ammunition sent by the king were checked over, it was found that De Caen had shamefully cheated his government. The musket powder was of bad quality. Two arquebuses, six feet long, with wheel locks, were in good condition, but 187 pounds of slow-match needed for firing them proved to be rotten. The fuse simply did not burn! Sixty-four sets of pikeman's armor had arm guards missing. "I'd like to get my hands on that double-dealing blackguard, De Caen," muttered Champlain. "It's lucky for him, he took to his heels without waiting for me to give him a receipt for these supplies."

Champlain was particularly concerned over the defenseless state of Quebec, because the settlement was steadily growing. The good Paris apothecary, Louis Hébert, was the first to establish a home and family on the St. Lawrence. Others followed fast. That girl who had waited so patiently for Daniel Haye was his wife now, and the sailor lad from St. Malo had grown to be a man whose farm was larger than the estate of many a nobleman back home. *Habitants*, Champlain called these people, and so the settlers along the St. Lawrence are called to this day.

Eustace Boullé had become the explorer's right-hand man. Champlain made him second in command at Quebec, and Eustace set to work to build the fort on the cliff. The plans called for thick stone walls, but earth, sod and logs would have to do for a time. Only eight men could be spared for the work, and Eustace went to live at the top of the cliff with them, so that no time should be lost in journeys up and down the steep road.

"I wish you wouldn't stay off by yourself like that," complained Hélène, who had hoped to see more of her brother. "I don't understand why you and Sam are in such a rush about finishing the fort. Everything is so peaceful here, and the Indians are so gentle and good."

Sam and Eustace exchanged glances. Hélène was happy teaching the Indian children to read at the big house the Franciscan Fathers had built, or at the still larger house belonging to the Jesuits. No need to tell her that all Indians were not good like the children who were learning to be Christians.

Privately, Champlain told his brother-in-law some disquieting news. A strange shallop had been seen on the river, and aboard her was a huge man who always went about with a mask over his face. No one could find out who he was, but he sold guns to the savages. By royal decree, the penalty for selling arms to Indians was death, but unscrupulous traders were willing to take the risk in order to get rich.

The weak government back in France was to blame for this situation. It was true that De Caen now headed a new fur company. With bribery, he and men like him had forced out Pontgravé and the honest merchants who were fighting bitterly for their rights in court. The king was nothing but a figurehead, but an ambitious young bishop named Richelieu was rising to power. Soon, he would become Cardinal Richelieu, and France would have a strong but ruthless leader.

Champlain did what he could, almost single-handed, in Canada. Right now he had a scheme most dear to his heart. He was negotiating a peace between the Iroquois and the St. Lawrence tribes. A lesser man would never have dreamed of such a thing, for it was like trying to make lions and tigers get along together. No Indian could remember the day when these tribes had not hated each other, and everyone freely predicted the scheme would fail.

Champlain set to work with great cleverness. A near-by tribe was looking for a new chief, and Champlain favored Miristou, a fine young man whose father and grandfather had been chiefs before him. So Sam gave a feast costing forty beaver skins. When the tribesmen had thoroughly gorged themselves with moose meat, he made them an election speech. Miristou became chief, and presented Champlain with sixty-five beaver skins — upon election.

The explorer lost no time in putting his peace ideas before the young chief. Miristou persuaded two Iroquois to come to Quebec, and Champlain presented them with thirty-five beaver skins' worth of European merchandise. They were to start peace talks back home among the Iroquois towns.

It cost many more beaver skins to bring the Iroquois to terms, but at last, rival chiefs smoked the pipe of peace. Four quiet, constructive years followed. For the first time in two generations, no Indian war party slipped through the forests or crossed the lakes by night. More than once,

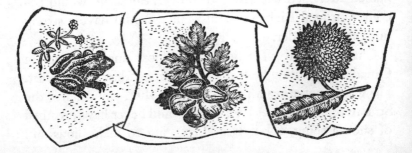

hotheaded young braves threatened to prove their valor by a raid, but Miristou found out in time and, with Champlain's help, put a stop to the mischief.

With Champlain in command, everyone at Quebec helped to improve the settlement. In winter, heavy logs were hauled over the snow to build a new and better *habitation*. Two carpenters were always busy repairing pinnaces and boats, while two more made doors and windows for the new house. Other less skilled workmen sawed boards, and fifteen hundred wide oak planks were ready by spring.

In May, a heavy gale blew the roof off the fort. Champlain had men and materials ready to repair it. And when the gable blew off Louis Hébert's stone house he got that repaired too, for his old friend.

By the spring of 1624, Champlain's journal contains such peaceful, homelike entries that his days of adventure seem to be over. The most exciting years lay just ahead, but right now, Sam wrote of wild cherries that began to bud in April. Perhaps Hélène asked him to put down the date, May 12, when she found the first white violets in the woods.

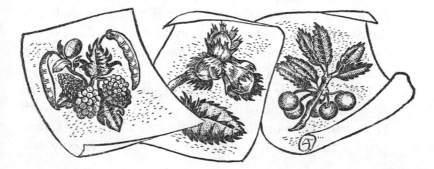

On May eighteenth, the apple trees brought over from France were budding.

"I want to remember these things and look for my flowers again next year," said Hélène. But in August, she and her husband sailed for France, after spending five winters at Quebec. This time Champlain spoke of sailing "with the fleet," for Canada had become so important that five or six vessels set out together!

One ship left the fleet when the shores of home were in sight. She had orders to proceed along the French coast to Bordeaux. Off Brittany, Turkish pirates caught her! All the men aboard her were sold into slavery at Constantinople. Suppose that ship had been ours, thought Champlain, when he learned of the incident.

While in Paris, Champlain was made lieutenant governor of Canada. The king gave him sweeping powers and made him many fine-sounding promises. But Sam would have preferred a small company of soldiers and a few guns for the fort at Quebec. Without these, he could not make Quebec a safe place for Hélène. Sadly, he said good-by to her, and she never returned to New France.

In March, 1625, Champlain went aboard the ship *Catherine* and sailed for Quebec. He was disgusted to find little done during his absence, especially at the fort. But Eustace Boullé was with him, next in command again. Together, they set to work.

Using materials already on the spot, they built a wall all around the edge of the high cliff. "I arranged it with two small demi-bastions, well flanked — " wrote Champlain — "the mountain does the rest. There is only one approach from the land side, and that a difficult one."

Four brass cannon were mounted so as to command the river. Then there were seven *perriers*, which were swivel guns used in firing stones. Two iron falconets completed the armament, but there were also four seven-foot arque-buses which could be rushed to any point along the walls where they were most needed.

Champlain was not satisfied with this assortment of arms, but it would have to do. From now on, he and Eustace lived at the fort in a little log block-house, where the Chateau Frontenac now stands. It was a joy to be high above the old market place, where the fur traders squabbled and cheated each other to their heart's content.

The fort was completed just in time. On the faraway Hudson River, five Dutch traders were killed by Iroquois — yet that evil deed endangered Quebec! The Dutch gave presents to Algonquins and Hurons, to get them to attack the Iroquois in revenge.

Champlain and his loyal friend, Chief Miristou, almost succeeded in keeping the peace. Then ten hotheaded young braves went on the warpath. Under pretense of friend-ship, they captured three Iroquois. One got away, but they brought two back to the St. Lawrence with the idea of torturing them. Champlain was actually able to persuade these young braves to let the prisoners alone: take one back — with presents — and keep the other as a hostage. He had gained tremendous influence with the savages since the day when all he could get was permission to shoot a dying victim.

Two Algonquins were sent into Iroquois country with

the returned captive and the gifts. For this dangerous mission, Champlain chose two braves who had been accused of murdering a white trader. The Iroquois promptly set upon them and killed them. "And so the scoundrels were themselves murdered," said Champlain, commenting on the justice of their fate.

But Miristou's powerful tribe was so angry at the death of their ambassadors that they literally tore their hostage to bits. Now war flared up along the rivers and lakes, like the terrible flame of a forest fire before a high wind. Champlain's own Indians were insolent to him, and he went about armed and watchful. All settlers were warned to be on the alert.

Spring came, but with it, no supply ships from France. This was such a common occurrence that Champlain was not worried at first. He did not know that, back in Europe, England and France were at war. Quebec was blockaded by the British fleet, and her settlers were left to starve.

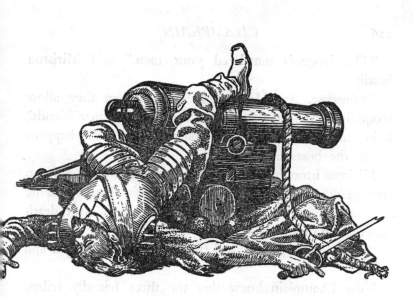

23 · FIRE AND SWORD

ON A grassy point just below Quebec was a small herd of
cattle, brought from France with great trouble and expense. They were doing well, and Champlain had a barn
built for them on Cape Tourmente, as the place was called.
A few settlers lived there, taking care of the cattle. One
day, two men set out to drive some cows to Quebec. One
was a servant, working for the Hébert family.

The men never arrived. When Champlain sent to learn
what had happened, his messengers found the bodies of
their comrades lying beside a small stream. The men had
been scalped — the cattle had disappeared.

Champlain sent for Miristou. "You must have better control over your tribes," he said. "White men are not to be
killed, and you know it."

"The Iroquois murdered your men," said Miristou hastily.

"Nonsense. Are Montagnais so weak that they allow Iroquois to come among their villages, killing their friends? Bring me hostages. And understand that if this happens again, the hostages shall die."

Miristou brought his own son, a boy of twelve, and two sons of other chiefs. "Learn of the White Father, for he has much wisdom," Miristou told his boy. "Meet death like the son of a chief — if death comes."

"I will, Father," promised the lad, standing straight and tall.

Now Champlain knew that the three friendly tribes, Hurons, Algonquins and Montagnais, were pledged not to harm the settlement. But suppose their chiefs could not control all the braves? He found himself praying with all his heart that order would be maintained, for he could never kill these children, no matter what happened. He kept his face stern and cold, lest Miristou should guess his thoughts.

When January came, a starving tribe of Montagnais arrived at Quebec, asking for food. "You should have thought of this when you took to killing white men," said Champlain. He ordered the palisade gates closed, and the Indians camped down outside to take council.

In a short time, a delegation waited upon the Sieur de Champlain at his headquarters in the fort. Ever since the man in the mask and other smugglers had been selling them guns, they had been insolent. Now, hunger made them very meek indeed. They brought three little girls from their tribe, which they proceeded to give to the White Father, not as hostages, but to keep!

During all the years Champlain had lived among Indians, such a thing had never before happened. Once Pontgravé wanted to take an Indian girl home for a servant to his wife. He was indignantly refused. Girls and women never went to Port Royal, except with men of their family. They were not allowed to go often, or stay long.

"I will adopt these children," promised Champlain, touched by the Indians' faith in him. "They shall be Christians, and I will have them taught to read and write and to do fine needlework, just as though they were my daughters."

It was a great disappointment to Champlain that he had no children of his own, and he was really glad to adopt these little Indian girls. He looked at them, standing there in their best deerskin skirts, their hair shining with sun-flower-seed oil, and with many strips of wampum around their necks. "I name you Faith, Hope and Charity," he said, with just the suspicion of a twinkle in his eyes.

The Indians were delighted with the way their gift had been received and still more pleased with a small bag of corn Champlain gave them. Now the whole tribe were children of the White Father, they said. But in a few days they returned in dismay, a weeping girl held firmly between two warriors. Faith, who was the oldest of Champlain's adopted daughters, had run away because she was homesick. "Now she understands that she no longer belongs to us," said the chief. "May the White Father not be angry. She will stay and be happy now." He gave the girl such a menacing scowl that she sobbed bitterly.

Champlain suppressed a smile at the way Faith obeyed the command to be happy. If she was homesick, he wanted her to go back to her people — but how could it be arranged without insulting the tribe?

Then he had a bright idea. Faith was fifteen, and as Indian girls grow up very quickly, perhaps she was in love with some young brave in her tribe. "As the father of this girl," he said, "it is my duty to arrange a marriage for her. Could you name some skillful young hunter who would be able to supply my daughter with good moose meat and plenty of beavers' tails? She is the daughter of a great chief, remember."

Instantly, Faith stopped crying. It seemed there was a certain brave. Champlain gave his daughter enough wampum to make her a princess in her own tribe, and somehow, the young Indian managed to kill a very thin deer for the marriage feast.

Charity, who was only eleven and Hope, who was twelve, said they would not go back to their tribe for the world. "Father Champlain," they called the man whom they loved just as dearly as white children love their own father. They learned French very fast and always spoke to Champlain using the affectionate "thou" instead of "you," which is the way French children talk to their parents.

Winter was over at last. With spring, there should come ships from France with provisions and letters from home. But it was the first of July when Champlain sat at his desk and wrote these words: "It is as though we had been deliberately abandoned."

There came a furious pounding on the door. Champlain jumped to open it, and Foucher, one of his most trusted men, staggered into the room. He had been sent to Cape Tourmente with food for three men, a woman and her little girl, who were living there, taking care of the cattle. Now here he was back again, breathless — disaster written plainly in his face.

"Is it the Indians?" cried Champlain. "Have they killed our people? What about Marguerite Martin and her little girl!" Then his face grew pale as he thought of the boy hostages he loved so much. "Please God it's not another Indian raid," he murmured.

Foucher shook his head. "Not Indians — the English!" he cried. "They have taken all our people prisoner, killed the cattle and burned the barns."

"Tell me how it happened," demanded Champlain, hardly able to believe his ears. Why on earth should the

English attack a handful of settlers and kill their cattle? He sent a servant for food, for Foucher was evidently exhausted.

"I was out among the barns just about daylight this morning," began Foucher. "Suddenly I saw men coming up through the trees. 'Halt!' I said — and I blessed the saints because I had brought my musket.

"But a French voice answered. 'We are friends. The provision ships have come from France and we bring letters from Monseigneur the Cardinal Richelieu to the Sieur de Champlain. Give us breakfast, will you? The wind has fallen and we have a long row up-river ahead of us.' "

Foucher paused and drank eagerly from the pewter mug the servant had brought. "What a fool I was!" he continued. "I rushed forward to greet these friends and found myself surrounded by English soldiers who had been hidden in the trees. There were sixteen men — to catch the four of us."

"What a compliment," said Champlain grimly. "But soldiers? This is no privateering raid, then. Is France at war with England?"

"Yes — so I learned when I was taken aboard an English pinnace. 'You are all prisoners of war,' they told us. We were not bound, so I jumped overboard and swam under water — a trick the savages taught me. They fired a few shots, all wide of the mark, and I found my canoe which luckily was well hid."

"Good man!" exclaimed Champlain. "Now we must warn the *habitants* and bid them take refuge in the fort."

"Daniel Haye is doing that, sir. I stopped at his cabin on my way up-river. His wife came along in my canoe, and soon Dan will be here with the Hébert family and other settlers."

A trumpet called all the people of Quebec together in the market place, a few moments later. Champlain spoke to them with more confidence than he could possibly feel. "I have just learned that our country is at war with England," he said. "The English are already in the river, and without doubt they mean to take Quebec. We cannot hope to hold the lower town, but let us dig trenches and prepare to sell it dearly.

"Fort St. Louis will be another matter. At my signal, we will abandon the settlement and climb the cliff road. Never fear, my friends, the fort on the hill will prove a hard nut to crack. Now, three rousing cheers for the Lilies of France."

A ragged cheer went up from the handful of half-starved settlers. They knew well how little food and ammunition they had but, somehow, Champlain gave them courage and made them think they had a chance to win. He assigned a post to each man and they spent the rest of the day practising what to do when the alarm came — and digging the trenches Champlain laid out. Women helped — and so did all the boys and girls, but little children were sent to the fort.

Next day a boat was seen, making for the St. Charles River, close to Quebec. Champlain sent some men through the woods with arquebuses. "Resist a landing and defeat them if you can," he ordered. "But keep well hidden among the trees, the way the savages would do, for we cannot afford to lose you. Perhaps the English mean to set fire to the house of the Holy Fathers, there by the river."

But Champlain's men recognized their comrades from Cape Tourmente as the boat drew near. The little girl was there too, with her mother, and they could not fire upon the skiff. A Basque fisherman came ashore with a letter for Champlain. Then the boat put out into the St. Lawrence again.

"We are 18 sail strong," said the letter. "I have seized the establishment at Tadoussac and all boats along shore. I had made preparations for going to see you, but thought it better to send an advice boat to destroy and seize your cattle, for I know that when you are in distress for want of food, I shall more easily take your settlement." The letter went on to discuss terms of surrender, and it was signed, DAVID KIRKE.

Champlain read the letter to Eustace and other leaders. "He ought not to menace us from so far," said Champlain. "Let this fellow Kirke come up-river and exchange a shot or two with us, at least."

The rest agreed, so they composed a letter for General Kirke. "It is true that the better a fortified place is provisioned, the better it holds out," wrote Champlain. "Nevertheless, the place can be made good with slender means, where good order prevails. That is the reason why, having still Indian corn, peas and beans, not to mention what the country produces, honor demands that we fight to the death."

A smile deepened the creases around Champlain's eyes. "Don't read this about the corn and beans, Eustace — it will make your mouth water."

Dipping his quill again, he continued his letter. "I know

you will think more highly of our courage if we firmly await the arrival of yourself and your forces than if, in a cowardly fashion, we abandoned something that is dear to us, without first making proof of your cannon, your approaches, entrenchments and batteries against this place, not easy of access."

Champlain chuckled. "That will give him pause. He can't stay here all winter digging trenches, and he knows it. Let's see now — one more good whopping lie about our food supply, perhaps."

Dipping his quill again, Champlain wrote, "As to the destruction of our cattle, it is a matter of a few beasts which in no way diminish what we depend on for a living."

"And how's this for the end? 'We are now waiting from hour to hour to receive you.' Pretty good — eh? I'll sign it."

Now they watched for the coming of General Kirke, but days went by and there was no sign of him. Kirke had been fooled by the letter, and he had sailed away without attacking Quebec. "This shows that it is a good thing to put on a bold countenance," said Champlain.

The winter that followed was one of terrible privation, however. Each man could have only seven ounces of dried peas a day. The settlers dared not shoot game, because they had only fifty pounds of powder, but the eel fishing was good and saved many lives.

When help still failed to come from France the following spring, Champlain made plans to evacuate Quebec. He had nearly a hundred people to take care of, and the

Indians living along the Kennebec River promised to take fifty white settlers to their town. An old pinnace, hardly fit for firewood, was repaired, and in it Eustace sailed for Canso with thirty more.

"You'll surely reach home aboard some Breton fisherman who dares to run the British blockade," Champlain encouraged. "Don't lose my letter to Hélène."

Eustace promised. "I'll see you in Paris," he said. Then he turned away hastily, for in his heart he never believed that Champlain would live to go back to France.

Sixteen men had volunteered to remain with Champlain at Quebec. Every day the two little Indian girls, Hope and Charity, went out with Father Champlain's servant to look for ground nuts. They could find a wild bean vine if any were growing, but now they had to walk twelve miles before coming to a patch of these plants, because the settlers had eaten all the roots near by.

Hope and Charity were walking along the shore of the St. Lawrence River. "Father Champlain says that soon the enemy will come," they told each other. This was easy for them to understand, since all their lives, their tribe had feared the Iroquois. Suddenly, Hope plucked at Charity's arm. "Look!" she cried. "Ships on the river!"

"Perhaps our king has sent a ship with food for us, and ammunition," said Champlain's servant.

"That flag is red with bars on it," said the Indian girls, who could see much farther than the white man. "Come. We must tell Father Champlain. It is the enemy." They turned and ran, but they did not forget the four little bags of roots they had gathered.

24 · ACTION ON THE RIVER

"IT WAS decided that, considering our helpless condition, we could not hold out," wrote Champlain. "The thing to do was to put on a bold front and ask for good terms of surrender." He called together his men. "If Kirke tries to land, we will show him the way to lose some men," Champlain told them. And the sixteen defenders of Quebec raised a cheer.

With a spyglass, the approaching invaders could see men standing valiantly beside their guns at the fort. The English decided not to attack, but sent a letter, under a white flag. This contained an order to surrender, signed by General David Kirke and his two brothers, Louis and Thomas.

On July 19, 1629, Samuel de Champlain wrote out his

articles of capitulation. "First show us the commission of your king and prove that this is an act of legitimate warfare. Convey all our companions back to France — also the two native girls who were given me by the savages, two years ago. I must be allowed to take them with me without any hindrance."

Always fair to everyone, Champlain wrote, "We had every kind of courtesy from the English. There was no burning or looting of Quebec." But Sam's face was full of grief as he watched the Lilies of France flutter down and the English flag rise over the fort on the river.

The *habitants* were given their choice of returning to France or remaining under British rule. If they remained, they were free to sell surplus crops, trade with the Indians, or trap animals and sell their pelts. The settlers looked at each other in frank amazement. Why their own government allowed only titled gentlemen who were members of the fur company to trade and make money!

"Out of friendship, they asked my advice," said Champlain, "but who could blame them if they choose to stay." He reminded them that the Holy Fathers were going home and that there would be no church. But in fairness, he added, "Burdened as you are with children, you would be beggars in France if you go there now. Why not work hard to raise crops here in Canada? In winter, you can go trapping and sell furs to the English. Then you can go home to France with money in your pockets and a chance to make a fresh start."

"By next year, the Sieur de Champlain will be back here, at the head of a French fleet," encouraged Daniel Haye.

"Let us stay and keep a welcome at Quebec for Champlain."

"Thank you, Dan," said Champlain, after the rest had gone. "You gave our people courage. Now if our government would only give her colonists the freedom these English offer! I will bring this matter to the king's attention but I fear the recapture of Quebec will be an easier matter than the winning of rights for poor men!"

Champlain was taken down the river to Tadoussac. "General Kirke refuses to let me go to France," he told Dan. "I am a prisoner of war and I believe they are taking me to a place called the Tower of London. At any rate, I shall get more to eat than seven ounces of dried peas a day."

As the English vessel sailed down the St. Lawrence, Champlain stood on deck, taking a last farewell of the river he loved. Suddenly, a wild hope of deliverance sprang to life in his heart. There, just ahead, was an armed French vessel. It was Émery de Caen, nephew of De Caen of the fur company, arriving at this late date with help for besieged Quebec! Champlain was ordered below decks and hatches were nailed down over his head while Captain Kirke prepared to fight.

De Caen was the first to open fire. Champlain heard the splintering crash of an iron cannon-ball tearing through the ship's rail. Another shot bounded along the deck, sounding like stage thunder. "Well aimed! *Vive la France!*" shouted Champlain, but of course no one could hear his voice above the roar of battle. Through a porthole, he managed to get a glimpse of the fight.

Captain Kirke's guns were answering now. He was clos-
ing with De Caen's vessel. "Ready with the grappling
hooks," yelled Kirke, and his men ran for great iron chains
with hooks to hold two vessels side by side. Kirke had
many more men than De Caen and he knew he could
board the enemy easily, once the ships were fastened together.

But in his excitement, the helmsman made a bad job of
coming alongside. He rammed the French ship, head on,
and the flukes of a great anchor caught in De Caen's rigging. Now the two vessels were fastened together indeed
but they were like two stags with antlers locked. Captain
Kirke tried to make his men board the enemy by running
along the bowsprit of their own ship. It was too much to
ask. They would be picked off, one by one, with musket
shots from the Frenchman's deck.

From his post at the porthole, Champlain could not tell
what had happened but he sensed the confusion from
sounds overhead. "Forward, comrades," he shouted, though
he knew his voice could not possibly reach his friends.
Why didn't De Caen take advantage of the delay — whatever might be the cause? But the French had no leader
like Champlain. In a few minutes, De Caen's voice could
be heard, calling, "Quarter! We surrender."

Champlain went over to a bunk and sat down, his face
in his hands. The little Indian girls came over to comfort
him. They were terrified but all through the fight they held
back their tears like the brave girls that they were. For
their sake, Champlain began to talk cheerfully of the journey ahead. "General Kirke will meet us at Tadoussac and

take us to London," he said. "Wait till you see that great walled city with its bridges and its castle by the Thames River!"

A rasping sound was heard overhead as nails were pulled out of the hatch cover. Champlain was allowed on deck again and soon Tadoussac was reached. Whom should he meet there but his brother-in-law, Eustace Boullé! The two friends gripped hands.

But the tale which Eustace had to tell was heartbreaking. He had come upon De Caen's ship anchored part way up the St. Lawrence with three months' supplies for Quebec. "Give me strong sailors in place of my starving men," urged Eustace, "and let me rush the supplies to the fort."

Evidently the nephew was as great a scoundrel as his uncle. Émery de Caen refused. Eustace got food for his men but many beaver skins were demanded in payment. De Caen was busy trading, he said. He would go up to Quebec when he got ready.

Leaving the old pinnace with De Caen, Eustace set out in De Caen's longboat. His men rowed well because the food had given them a little strength, while the news that help was coming lifted their spirits. Close to shore, they sighted a vessel. "We came on softly, hoping with all our hearts that she was French," said Eustace. "Then we heard a sailor singing: —

> With cutlass and gun, they fought hours three
> Cruising the coast of High Barbary.

The words were English so we knew we must slip by unseen. Our men put their backs into it and rowed hard. Then, just as we were pulling behind the Isle of Orleans, the English spotted us. They put a boat over and caught us easily for we were unarmed and our men were exhausted."

Surely this is the last of the bad news, thought Sam. But one more blow awaited him. General Kirke sent for him to discuss the articles of surrender which Champlain and Kirke's brothers had signed. "I agree to everything except this business of the Indian girls," said General Kirke. "You may not take them out of the country. It will make trouble with the savages."

In vain, Champlain explained that the children were his by adoption. Since he had been allowed to keep his personal belongings, he had one thousand English pounds' worth of beaver skins. "Give these to the Montagnais tribe, if you wish," he offered. But Kirke would not listen.

At first the girls cried and refused to eat. Hope went to General Kirke. "The Sieur de Champlain is truly our dear father," she said. "He gave us food, taking what he needed himself to live. He clothes us and cares for us always."

Still General Kirke refused to let the Indian girls go with Champlain. Seeing that it was useless to argue any more, Champlain chose a red cloak and a velvet dressing gown of his own and had them made into dresses for Hope and Charity. He talked with them and made them promise to be good girls and say the prayers he had taught them.

Charity asked for a rosary and her "Father Champlain" gave her one. Luckily, Eustace had one he could give to Hope. "We never gave one anything without giving the other the same," explained Champlain.

Dan had said good-by to his friend at Quebec but he had followed Kirke's ship in his canoe all the way to Tadoussac. Now he found that there was something he could do for Champlain. "If the little girls are willing, I will take them home to my wife," he offered. "Jeanne will love them like a mother and bring them up with our own children till you come back."

For the first time in many days, Champlain's weather-beaten face broke into a smile. "God bless you, Dan! I could not leave my little girls in better hands." He called Hope and Charity and explained to them that they were to live with Daniel Haye.

"We will not leave you, any more than we would Monsieur de Champlain, our father," said the girls. "We will obey you as we would our father."

Since Quebec was lost in the end, Champlain asked himself if the previous year of starvation had been worth while. His magnificent bluff had worked and Kirke put off capture for a season. But did it matter?

When General Kirke reached Plymouth, England, Champlain had his answer. Peace had been declared three months before Quebec was captured! The self-sacrifice had saved the fort after all. Of course Champlain was a prisoner of war no longer. He hastened to London to see the French ambassador. "Quebec will be restored to France at once," said the ambassador. "England does not dispute our right to New France."

The ambassador smiled. "A book called *The Voyages of the Sieur de Champlain* has helped to establish French claims. It was published before any dispute arose, you see."

Once more, Champlain's services to his country had not been in vain.

But weeks went by and the French government did nothing. De Caen came to London looking for his beaver skins — but Louis XIII never so much as asked for his colony of Quebec.

Champlain went to France where he soon discovered that Cardinal Richelieu was the real head of the nation, and not the king. The cardinal assured Champlain that Quebec would be restored but seemed in no hurry to begin negotiations. As to building a better fort on the St. Lawrence and arming it properly — that would cost a great deal of money. Certainly a strong trading post was desirable — but it could wait.

Sick at heart, Champlain went to his old home in Brouage. But when he arrived, he hardly knew the place. The salt farmers were still at work, to be sure, and the tide still glistened on a wide expanse of sand. But instead of a sleepy little town, Champlain found a great stone fortress with seven towers. He entered Brouage by an iron gate to find the winding streets all swept away and wide avenues, crossing at right angles, taking their place.

"Why all this?" demanded Champlain as he examined ramparts and ditches, an arsenal and storehouses. He learned that Cardinal Richelieu was sparing no expense to defend himself against the French Protestants of near-by La Rochelle.

If only this beautiful fortress could have been built at Quebec, thought Champlain. France should protect her people — not arm herself against them. Samuel de Champlain was always a firm believer in religious freedom. As a young man, he had fought for Henry of Navarre, then a Protestant. He was proud when King Henry signed the Edict of Nantes, giving freedom of religion to all France. Now it seemed as if gains were lost and progress ended.

Three long years went by, while Champlain labored for the restoration of Quebec. He would have preferred a dozen battles with the Iroquois to those tedious interviews with courtiers, lawyers and foreign ambassadors. "If I ever return to Quebec, I will build a church," he promised, kneeling before the altar in the great cathedral of Notre Dame in Paris. "The church shall be called 'Our Lady of Recovery.' "

In 1633, this prayer was granted and Samuel de Champlain became Governor of New France and Commander of the fort at Quebec. The *Don de Dieu*, or Gift of God, was the name of the vessel in which he sailed to take over Canada.

Guns from the fort echoed over the St. Lawrence as the new governor's pinnace came in sight. Somehow, word had spread to the northernmost tribes of Indians that the White Father was coming home. The narrows opposite Quebec were black with Indian canoes.

Already, the Lilies of France fluttered from Fort St. Louis. Who should come to greet Champlain but the surly, unscrupulous De Caen! This time, however, he bowed low, as he handed over the keys to the fortress. Champlain had the power to make him behave from now on, and he knew it.

Feasts for the Indians lasted three days and three nights

with more and more hungry guests arriving all the time. Champlain always knew when to spend plenty of beaver skins, so Hurons, Algonquins and Montagnais went off to their lodges full of moose meat, vowing eternal friendship with the White Father.

When the shouts and the weird chanting died away and the ceremonial dances were over, Champlain found his old friend, Daniel Haye, waiting for him at the fort. With him were two pretty Indian girls who ran to kiss Champlain's hands. "Father," cried Hope and Charity, "we have been good children! And you have come back, just as you promised."

25 · CHRISTMAS NIGHT

ONCE more, Quebec was falling to pieces from neglect but Champlain went right to work, bringing fresh enthusiasm to the task. The old *habitation* by the river was not worth rebuilding and Champlain made the fort on the cliff the center of the colony. He began to build in stone instead of wood, now that he had better workmen and more money at his command. First came the church which he had promised back in France to establish. It was a great day when Champlain went to celebrate mass in Our Lady of Recovery for the first time.

The new Governor of Canada had no time for exploration but he delighted in sending young men out with the Indians. Each was given a careful letter of instruction, telling what to look for, what questions to ask savages and what notes to bring back.

Jean Nicolet had lived among the tribes for fifteen years. He came to Champlain and offered to do some exploring. "Go to Lake Huron," Champlain directed. "Then travel west and tell me what lies beyond."

"There is another great lake, Monsieur de Champlain," reported Jean when he returned from his journey. And he told of Lake Michigan. Champlain was like a boy again in his enthusiasm as he got out his old map and added the new discovery from Jean's notes.

With Champlain in complete authority over the fur company, the smuggling of arms to the Indians was practically stopped. A new kind of company was also formed and in this Champlain invested a good deal of money. This was a company to bring colonists to New France. Like the ardent promoter that he was, Champlain wrote out some information to be printed in Paris.

"He who will have thirty acres of cleared land, with the help of a few cattle, hunting and fishing and trading with the Indians, can live here with a family of ten. He will be as well off as those men in France who have an income of fifteen or twenty thousand pounds a year."

Champlain smiled with satisfaction as he read over the part about trading with the Indians. How hard he had worked to win that right for his people! But the victory was his and now a poor man could trade in furs the same as a nobleman. This was a step in the right direction and he frankly admitted that the English pointed the way. Someday, the New World would stand for freedom — for equal rights for all.

In 1634, the first boatload of new settlers sailed up the St. Lawrence. They were led by a surgeon named Robert Giffard who had been in Canada before and understood conditions. These people brought their wives and children. They came properly equipped with farm tools, cattle and supplies so that they could establish permanent homes. What a contrast they made to those young noblemen back at Port Royal who brought nothing but fowling pieces and a box of dice! In 1634, many a hard-working young farmer found his passage money paid by Champlain.

The Franciscan Fathers did not return to Quebec. The fur company refused to help two religious orders and the Jesuits had the support of Cardinal Richelieu. They built a college at Quebec and a school for Indian children. A Jesuit Mission was established up the St. Lawrence at Three Rivers and another on Cape Breton on the St. Lawrence Gulf.

In order to gain government support for his colony, Champlain knew just how to handle Cardinal Richelieu. He always addressed him in terms which that supreme egoist could understand. "Your *Grandieur*," Champlain called him — and went on to make his report.

"I have improved our fortifications, increased the bastions and raised two new buildings. Quebec now commands the whole river, it being impossible for a boat to go up or down without being stopped. A new fort has been built on an island which I have named 'Isle de Richelieu' as a perpetual reminder that these colonies are under the protection of Your Greatness." Champlain went on to ask for "six twenties of men" — as he put it. "The cost would be very little and I ask it of you, My Lord, who can do anything he pleases."

This letter is a contrast to the respectful but friendly letters Champlain used to write to King Henry. The great cardinal was too conceited to notice the sarcasm with which Champlain referred to his dictatorship. About half the men asked for arrived, which was more than Champlain expected. Good arms and ammunition were sent also, and never again would sixteen starving men be left to hold the fort alone.

Although Champlain never made trade his chief interest, he was now a wealthy man. He used his money to help Indians who came to Quebec hungry but who never left without some bags of corn. Settlers who found the going hard soon learned that they could depend on the governor for a helping hand. And the Church of Our Lady of Recovery was built and maintained entirely at Champlain's expense.

Samuel de Champlain still carried the scars of Indian arrows. He still remembered being shipwrecked not once but many times and he remembered how men had almost killed him during the first days at Quebec. But his last years were peaceful ones.

It was a winter's night and Dan had come to the fort to spend an evening with his old friend. He found Champlain turning over the pages of one of the books he had written about his adventures. He had come to his "Treatise on Seamanship."

"What a young man I was when I wrote this," he said, showing Dan the book. Now he was sixty-eight years old.

"Read it to me, won't you?" suggested Dan.

And Champlain began, smiling to remember his first years as Captain of the *St. Julien.* "A good captain must be hardy and active; untiring in his work. He should be liberal, according to his opportunities, and courteous to defeated enemies — keeping faith if he, himself, has made terms of surrender. He should not practise cruelty or be revengeful." Champlain paused to look into the bright flames of the fire which burned on the hearth.

"You have always been the 'good captain,'" said Dan. "This is a portrait of yourself."

"It was a young man's ideal," smiled Sam. "But we have fought the good fight." He turned his head as a faint tapping sound was heard against the casement. "It has begun to snow again. Let us be thankful we have warm homes, now, instead of those huts on St. Croix Island. But you must hurry back to your family. As for me" — Sam's eyes twinkled — "somehow the 'untiring captain' is weary tonight. I am going to bed."

They called the priest when Champlain could not rise from his bed next day. He was paralyzed, perhaps as a result of a past injury, but he did not suffer. "I have made my peace with God," he said, smiling at the friends who gathered around. "I have blazed the trail. Now the New World belongs to you who follow me."

On Christmas night, 1635, the bells began to toll at the Church of Our Lady of Recovery. The Father of Canada was dead.

Daniel Haye's children were singing carols in their home by the St. Lawrence. Faintly, their mother heard the bells. "Hush," she said. "Our dear Champlain is gone."

But after everyone had said a prayer for the friend they loved, Dan told his children to finish their song. "Champlain would like that," he said.

"Noël, Noël," sang the children.

ACKNOWLEDGMENT

THE AUTHOR appreciates the courtesy of the Champlain Society in giving permission to use material presented both in French and English in their edition of Champlain's works. All direct quotations from the writings of Samuel de Champlain are taken from this source. Translations of the poetry of Marc Lescarbot are the author's own, taken from the original French also found in *The Works of Samuel de Champlain*, edited by the Champlain Society.

The artist has included in his illustrations for the book some redrawings of Champlain's own sketches and plans, from the Champlain Society's edition of *The Works of Samuel de Champlain*.

Champlain In The New World

N E W   F R A
(CANADA)

Lake Superior

Lake Michigan

Lake Nipissing

Ottawa River

Isle de S
(Mo

(Georgian Bay)

Freshwater Sea
(Lake Huron)

(Lake Simcoe)

Lake of Onondagas
(Lake Ontario)

Lake Onei

Lake Erie

The Names In Parentheses On The
Map Are Those We Use Today.
They Were Not Known In Champlain's Time.